Treasures

Tested

ELL
Practice and Assessment

Macmillan
McGraw-Hill

B

The McGraw·Hill Companies

Macmillan
McGraw-Hill

Published by Macmillan/McGraw-Hill, of McGraw-Hill Education, a division of The McGraw-Hill Companies, Inc.,
Two Penn Plaza, New York, New York 10121.

Printed in the United States of America
3 4 5 6 7 8 9 10   021   09 08 07

Contents

Introduction

The ELL Practice and Assessment is designed to give English Language Learners practice with the skills taught throughout the unit. It provides teachers with a way to assess student mastery of these skills and to monitor student progress throughout the year. The practice pages, tests, and pages for recording student progress cover the following domains in grades 1–6:

- Reading Comprehension Strategies and Skills
- Phonics Strategies
- Vocabulary Strategies
- Grammar
- Writing skills
- Oral Language Development

Student Profile: Language Development

For each unit, the teacher will record observations of students' progress towards mastering the Language Objectives for each of the five weeks, along with students' strengths and weaknesses in the skills covered in that unit.

Student Profile: Strategy and Skill Assessment

For each unit, the teacher will record skill-specific results for the Weekly Tests and the Unit Progress Test to determine each student's level (Beginning, Intermediate, Advanced) for the next unit.

Yearly Language Record

Throughout the year, the teacher will use this form to record each student's level-specific responses to the Think and Compare questions in the Comprehension Check section of each ELL Leveled Reader. This record will enable instruction tailored to the child's individual needs using the differentiated instruction strategies in the teacher's edition.

Writing Rubric

Each week, the teacher will use the information in this rubric to assess the student's progress in writing during the Writing Workshop (grades 3–6) or 5-Day Writing (grades 1–2). The student's writing will be evaluated on ideas and content, organization, voice, word choice, sentence fluency, and conventions of written English.

Student Writing Profile

For each unit, the teacher will record the student's writing results from the Writing Workshop or 5-Day Writing, along with areas of strength and weakness.

Fiction and Nonfiction Book Talks

During Week 6 of each unit, students will present fiction or nonfiction Book Talks about the ELL Leveled Readers for the unit. Students will review the ELL Leveled Readers and weekly skills during this group activity. They will then answer skill-related book talk questions, and present their answers, along with a visual aid, to the class.

Peer Assessment

During the Book Talk presentations, selected students will assess their classmates' presentation. They will tell about their favorite part of the presentation, their classmates' areas of strength, and areas which need improvement.

Self-Assessment

After each unit, students will assess their progress by identifying their own areas of strength and weakness. This is also a good opportunity for students to set goals for themselves for the upcoming unit.

Practice Pages

The practice pages for each unit allow children to practice the skills for that week. Students will complete a vocabulary and phonics skill practice page on the second day of instruction, and a comprehension and grammar skill practice page on the fourth day of instruction. The students will work on these pages together as a class.

Study Guide for Unit Progress Test

The Study Guide covers the key skills of the unit and gives children a chance to review and practice the specific skills included on the Unit Progress Test. The first page of the Study Guide is a study aid to review skills previously taught, and the second, a practice page.

Administering the Weekly Tests and Unit Progress Tests

Each two-page Weekly Test consists of vocabulary, phonics, comprehension and grammar questions. Questions may require students to circle the correct word, match items to the correct answer, or write an appropriate sentence or constructed response.

The Unit Progress Test is a four-page test that reflects the skills addressed in the Weekly Tests. This test includes multiple-choice items as well as reading passages with constructed-response questions. The content of these reading passages is drawn from the unit theme.

General Procedures

Before the test: Distribute copies of the Weekly Test or Unit Progress Test. Review the test with the students. Read the directions as a class, and answer any questions that they may have. You may want to explain each section of these tests to students the first time you administer them.

During the test: Make sure that each student is following the directions and writing responses in the correct places. Answer questions about procedures and materials, but do not assist students with answering test items. If the test includes a listening selection, check to be sure that all students are on the same page, and read it aloud as students read along silently. Give students as much time as you think is necessary to finish the test. Remind the students to check their work before you collect the test.

Scoring Instructions

Using Results to Inform Instruction

Use the results of the Weekly Tests and Unit Progress Tests as a formative assessment tool to help monitor student progress. Information gathered by evaluating the results of this assessment can also be used to determine specific strengths and weaknesses of your students. If scores from the Weekly Tests are used to help determine report card grades, then you can consider this a summative assessment as well.

The primary focus of the Weekly Test and the Unit Progress Test is to measure student progress toward mastery of each skill. Scores that fall below the 80th percentile suggest that students require additional instruction in order to master that skill.

Using the Student Evaluation Charts

For each unit, there are several pages that will assist you in evaluating your ELL students. For each of the following, you will need to label a page for each student.

- The **Student Profile:** The **Language Development** page lists the language objectives for each week of every unit. Here you can make anecdotal records on the child's progress towards the language objectives. Beneath each language objective, write your observations of the child's language development as it pertains to that week's objective. Record any strengths or weaknesses that you have observed in the child's oral language patterns.

- The **Student Profile:** The **Strategy and Skill Assessment** page lists all of the skills covered on the Weekly Tests and Unit Progress Test, and the number of questions that assess each skill. In the Weekly Test section, in the column for each week, fill in the number of questions answered correctly for each skill. Count the total number of correct responses, and write the number correct above the total possible score. Follow the same procedure for the Unit Progress Test Section.

- The **Yearly Language Record** is a chart with spaces for you to assess the students' responses to the Think and Compare questions in the Comprehension Check sections in each unit. After asking each of the three questions for that week, write "B" for "Beginning," "I" for "Intermediate," or "A" for "Advanced." In the "Total" column, determine the type of response that the student gave the majority of the time, and record that letter. Write any additional comments on the lines provided. Refer to the Comprehension Check section in the teacher's guide for examples of Beginning, Intermediate, and Advanced responses.

- The **Writing Rubric** will help you to assess writing pieces that students produce during the Writing Workshop or 5-Day Writing. For each of the categories on the rubric, read the description for each level (Excellent, Good, Fair, Unsatisfactory) and circle the level that the student has attained.

- The **Student Writing Profile** is a place to record the student's writing scores. For each week, write the student's score in each category over the total possible score. Then, add the scores for each category and write the total in the Total box. Record any comments on the student's writing on the lines provided.

Evaluating the Scores

Evaluating the results of the above assessments provides specific information about students' daily instructional needs. We recommend that you use these results for instructional planning and re-teaching opportunities. Compare these results with your own observations of students' work and identify objectives that still need reinforcement. Incorporate these into your instructional plans for the coming week for individual, small group, or whole group instruction as indicated.

Language Development

Student Name _____

Record weekly Language Objective observations.

WEEK 1	Seek information about appropriate language use and behavior.

WEEK 2	Explain actions.

WEEK 3	Self-monitor and self-evaluate language development.

WEEK 4	Share social and cultural traditions and values.

WEEK 5	Understand and produce technical vocabulary and text features.

Areas of Strength	**Areas of Weakness**

Strategy and Skill Assessment

Student Name _____

Unit 1 Weekly Test Results

	WEEK 1	WEEK 2	WEEK 3	WEEK 4	WEEK 5
Vocabulary	/5	/5	/4	/5	/5
Phonics	/6	/6	/7	/6	/6
Comprehension	/3	/3	/2	/4	/4
Grammar	/4	/2	/3	/2	/5
Total	/18	/16	/16	/17	/20

Unit 1 Progress Test Results

VOCABULARY	
Use context clues to complete sentences	/3
Vocabulary Total	/3

PHONICS	
Short and long vowels	/4
r-controlled vowels	/4
Phonics Total	/8

EDITING	
Correct run-on sentences	/1
Correct sentence fragments	/2
Correct commas in a sentence	/3
Editing Total	/6

COMPREHENSION	
Identify main idea and details	/2
Identify character, plot, and setting	/1
Identify cause and effect	/1
Comprehension Total	4

GRAMMAR	
Identify correct independent and dependent clauses	/4
Identify correct conjunctions to make compound sentences	/3
Grammar Total	/7

TOTAL	/28

© Macmillan/McGraw-Hill

Student Name _____

Record weekly Language Objective observations.

WEEK 1	Respond to and use idioms appropriately.

WEEK 2	Seeking information about appropriate language use.

WEEK 3	Analyze, synthesize, and infer from information.

WEEK 4	Persuade, argue, negotiate, evaluate, and justify.

WEEK 5	Explore alternative ways of saying things.

Areas of Strength	Areas of Weakness
_____	_____
_____	_____
_____	_____

© Macmillan/McGraw-Hill

Strategy and Skill Assessment

Student Name _____

Unit 2 Weekly Test Results

	WEEK 1	WEEK 2	WEEK 3	WEEK 4	WEEK 5
Vocabulary	/6	/3	/5	/4	/3
Phonics	/5	/3	/5	/4	/3
Comprehension	/1	/4	/5	/4	/4
Grammar	/2	/2	/3	/4	/2
Total	/14	/12	/18	/16	/12

Unit 2 Progress Test Results

VOCABULARY	
Identify idiom	/2
Vocabulary Total	/6

PHONICS	
V/CV, VC/V, and VC/CV patterns	/6
Plurals	/4
Phonics Total	/10

EDITING	
Correct underlining	/1
Correct capitalization	/2
Correct abbreviations	/1
Correct plural forms	/2
Editing Total	/6

COMPREHENSION	
Make inferences	/3
Identify sequence	/1
Comprehension Total	/4

GRAMMAR	
Identify correct appositives	/2
Identify correct common and proper nouns	/2
Identify correct possessive nouns	/2
Grammar Total	/6

TOTAL	/32

© Macmillan/McGraw-Hill

Language Development

Student Name _____

Record weekly Language Objective observations.

WEEK 1	Share social and cultural traditions and values.

WEEK 2	Use a variety of writing styles appropriately for different audiences, purposes, and settings.

WEEK 3	Represent information visually and interpret information presented visually.

WEEK 4	Take notes to record important information and aid one's own learning.

WEEK 5	Self-monitor and self-evaluate language use according to setting and audience.

Areas of Strength	Areas of Weakness

Strategy and Skill Assessment

Student Name _____

Unit 3 Weekly Test Results

	WEEK 1	WEEK 2	WEEK 3	WEEK 4	WEEK 5
Vocabulary	/6	/4	/5	/4	/5
Phonics	/5	/4	/4	/5	/5
Comprehension	/3	/3	/2	/4	/5
Grammar	/3	/3	/3	/4	/4
Total	/17	/14	/14	/17	/19

Unit 3 Progress Test Results

VOCABULARY	
Use context clues to complete sentences	/6
Vocabulary Total	/6

PHONICS	
/ər/, /əl/, /ən/	/10
Phonics Total	/10

EDITING	
Correct punctuation of a play	/3
Correct capitalization of proper nouns	/3
Editing Total	/6

COMPREHENSION	
Summarize	/2
Identify character, plot, and setting	/1
Draw conclusions	/1
Comprehension Total	/4

GRAMMAR	
Identify correct linking verbs	/2
Identify correct predicate nouns and adjectives	/2
Identify correct action verbs	/1
Identify correct direct and indirect objects	/1
Grammar Total	/6

TOTAL	/32

© Macmillan/McGraw-Hill

Student Name_____

Record weekly Language Objective observations.

WEEK 1	Explore alternative ways of saying things.

WEEK 2	Demonstrate knowledge of acceptable classroom behaviors.

WEEK 3	Compare and contrast information.

WEEK 4	Express personal needs, feelings, and ideas.

WEEK 5	Participate in full class, group, and pair discussions.

Areas of Strength	Areas of Weakness
_____	_____
_____	_____
_____	_____

Strategy and Skill Assessment

Student Name _____

Unit 4 Weekly Test Results

	WEEK 1	WEEK 2	WEEK 3	WEEK 4	WEEK 5
Vocabulary	/4	/5	/6	/5	/6
Phonics	/6	/5	/5	/4	/5
Comprehension	/4	/2	/4	/3	/3
Grammar	/3	/3	/3	/4	/5
Total	/17	/15	/18	/16	/19

Unit 4 Progress Test Results

VOCABULARY	
Use context clues to complete sentences	/6
Vocabulary Total	/6

PHONICS	
Suffixes	/10
Phonics Total	/10

EDITING	
Correct use of *they, their, they're*	/3
Correct pronoun agreement	/3
Editing Total	/6

COMPREHENSION	
Identify fact and opinion	/1
Identify author's purpose	/2
Compare and contrast	/1
Comprehension Total	/4

GRAMMAR	
Identify correct indefinite pronouns	/4
Identify correct pronoun-verb	/3
Grammar Total	/7

TOTAL	/33

© Macmillan/McGraw-Hill

Language Development

Student Name _____

Record weekly Language Objective observations.

WEEK 1	Share social and cultural traditions and values.

WEEK 2	Self-monitor and self-evaluate language use according to setting and audience.

WEEK 3	Demonstrate knowledge through application in a variety of contexts.

WEEK 4	Describe, read about or participate in a favorite activity.

WEEK 5	Listen to, speak, read, and write about subject matter information.

Areas of Strength	Areas of Weakness

Strategy and Skill Assessment

Student Name _____

Unit 5 Weekly Test Results

	WEEK 1	WEEK 2	WEEK 3	WEEK 4	WEEK 5
Vocabulary	/5	/4	/4	/4	/5
Phonics	/4	/4	/4	/4	/5
Comprehension	/4	/4	/2	/3	/3
Grammar	/5	/5	/3	/3	/4
Total	/18	/17	/13	/14	/17

Unit 5 Progress Test Results

VOCABULARY	
Identify antonyms	/3
Vocabulary Total	/6

PHONICS	
Homophones	/8
Greek and Latin roots	/2
Phonics Total	/10

EDITING	
Correct use of irregular comparative forms	/3
Correct capitalization	/3
Editing Total	/6

COMPREHENSION	
Author's purpose	/1
Summarize	/1
Make judgments	/1
Main idea	/1
Comprehension Total	/4

GRAMMAR	
Compare using *more* and *most*	/2
Compare using *good* and *bad*	/2
Identify correct articles	/3
Grammar Total	/7

	TOTAL	/33

© Macmillan/McGraw-Hill

Language Development

Student Name _____

Record weekly Language Objective observations.

WEEK 1	**Analyze, synthesize, and infer from information.**

WEEK 2	**Listen to and imitate how others use English.**

WEEK 3	**Respond to and use slang appropriately.**

WEEK 4	**Formulate and ask questions.**

WEEK 5	**Express needs, feelings, and ideas.**

Areas of Strength	**Areas of Weakness**
_____	_____
_____	_____
_____	_____

© Macmillan/McGraw-Hill

Strategy and Skill Assessment

Student Name _____

Unit 6 Weekly Test Results

	WEEK 1	WEEK 2	WEEK 3	WEEK 4	WEEK 5
Vocabulary	/3	/4	/4	/4	/5
Phonics	/4	/4	/4	/5	/4
Comprehension	/5	/5	/2	/2	/2
Grammar	/4	/2	/5	/4	/3
Total	/16	/15	/15	/15	/14

Unit 6 Progress Test Results

VOCABULARY	
Identify multiple meaning words	/2
Vocabulary Total	/6

PHONICS	
Absorbed prefixes	/10
Phonics Total	/10

EDITING	
Correct use of commas	/2
Correct use of end punctuation	/3
Correct use of quotations	/1
Editing Total	/6

COMPREHENSION	
Identify theme	/2
Identify description	/1
Identify problem and solution	/1
Comprehension Total	/4

GRAMMAR	
Identify adjectives and adverbs	/2
Identify prepositional phrases	/2
Identify correct negative forms	/3
Grammar Total	/7

TOTAL	/33

© Macmillan/McGraw-Hill

Student Name _____

Record weekly comprehension check results.
Mark *B* for Beginning, *I* for Intermediate, *A* for Advanced

Week 1	Unit 1	Unit 2	Unit 3	Unit 4	Unit 5	Unit 6
Question 1						
Question 2						
Question 3						

Week 2	Unit 1	Unit 2	Unit 3	Unit 4	Unit 5	Unit 6
Question 1						
Question 2						
Question 3						

Week 3	Unit 1	Unit 2	Unit 3	Unit 4	Unit 5	Unit 6
Question 1						
Question 2						
Question 3						

Week 4	Unit 1	Unit 2	Unit 3	Unit 4	Unit 5	Unit 6
Question 1						
Question 2						
Question 3						

Week 5	Unit 1	Unit 2	Unit 3	Unit 4	Unit 5	Unit 6
Question 1						
Question 2						
Question 3						

TOTAL						

Additional Comments _____
_____
_____
_____

Scoring Rubric

4 Excellent	**3** Good	**2** Fair	**1** Unsatisfactory
Ideas and Content Content is strong and meaningful, ideas clearly and vividly expressed	**Ideas and Content** Supplies some good ideas or information, relative to genre of writing, purpose clear	**Ideas and Content** Some good ideas or information, but is somewhat lacking in purpose of message	**Ideas and Content** Student does not grasp intention of writing assignment, does not provide meaningful content
Organization Writing is highly coherent and well developed, relative to demands of this genre of writing	**Organization** Shows basic grasp of organization for this genre, assists in communicating writer's message	**Organization** Some organization evident, but some parts of writing lack organization of thought	**Organization** Has not presented message in organized fashion, lack of organization hinders reader's understanding
Voice Engaging, distinctive, clearly shows writer's interest in expressing message	**Voice** Clearly shows writer's interest in message	**Voice** Not very engaging, shows some interest in communicating message	**Voice** Flat, writer appears disinterested in communicating message
Word Choice Uses vivid, direct, and expressive words, or uses words that help to convey writer's message, appropriate to this genre	**Word Choice** Uses some expressive words, and uses words accurately	**Word Choice** Uses a few expressive words, uses some words inaccurately	**Word Choice** Does not use expressive or precise words, makes several mistakes in usage
Sentence Fluency Sentences are well constructed and flow well, writer varies sentence length, appropriate to genre of writing	**Sentence Fluency** Sentences are well constructed. Some variety of sentence length used, when appropriate	**Sentence Fluency** Sentences are properly constructed, but lack variety or flow	**Sentence Fluency** Writes irregular, incomplete, or non-syntactical sentences which don't meet the standards of this genre
Conventions Shows excellent grasp of grammar, spelling, punctuation and all conventions of standard written English (particularly those reviewed in this writing workshop)	**Conventions** Few errors in spelling, grammar and other conventions	**Conventions** Contains several errors in grammar, spelling, or other conventions, but these do not hinder reader's understanding	**Conventions** Writing contains many errors, which interfere with reader's understanding and appreciation of writing

© Macmillan/McGraw-Hill

Writing Assessment

Student Name _____ Unit _____

WEEK 1	SCORE
Ideas and Content	/4
Organization	/4
Voice	/4
Word Choice	/4
Sentence Fluency	/4
Conventions	/4
TOTAL	/24

WEEK 4	SCORE
Ideas and Content	/4
Organization	/4
Voice	/4
Word Choice	/4
Sentence Fluency	/4
Conventions	/4
TOTAL	/24

WEEK 2	SCORE
Ideas and Content	/4
Organization	/4
Voice	/4
Word Choice	/4
Sentence Fluency	/4
Conventions	/4
TOTAL	/24

WEEK 5	SCORE
Ideas and Content	/4
Organization	/4
Voice	/4
Word Choice	/4
Sentence Fluency	/4
Conventions	/4
TOTAL	/24

WEEK 3	SCORE
Ideas and Content	/4
Organization	/4
Voice	/4
Word Choice	/4
Sentence Fluency	/4
Conventions	/4
TOTAL	/24

COMMENTS: _____

_____

_____

_____

_____

_____

_____

Pick your role.

Leader	Recorder	Time Keeper	Helper	Motivator
Make sure students perform their roles.	Write down the group's answers.	Make sure your group finishes on time.	Gather materials. Ask teacher for help.	Encourage group members.

REMEMBER

- Take turns talking and listening.
- Share your ideas.
- Explain your thinking.
- Show respect for others.

Work with your group to answer the questions. You will read your answers to the class.

1. What is the title of the book?
2. Who is the author?
3. Describe the main character.
4. What is the setting?
5. What was one problem the characters had in the story?
6. What was the solution to the problem?
7. What was one thing that caused something else to happen?
8. What were your favorite parts of the book?

Pick your role.

Leader	Recorder	Time Keeper	Helper	Motivator
Make sure students perform their roles.	Write down the answers.	Make sure your group finishes on time.	Gather materials. Ask teacher for help.	Encourage group members.

REMEMBER

- Take turns talking and listening.
- Share your ideas.
- Explain your thinking.
- Show respect for others.

Work with your group to answer the questions. You will read your answers to the class.

1. What is the title of the book?
2. Who is the author?
3. What is the book about?
4. What did you learn about this topic?
5. What did you know about this topic from your own life?
6. What else would you like to learn about this topic?
7. What was the main idea?
8. Tell three details that support the main idea.

Pick your role.

Leader	Recorder	Time Keeper	Helper	Motivator
Make sure students perform their roles.	Write down the group's answers.	Make sure your group finishes on time.	Gather materials. Ask teacher for help.	Encourage group members.

REMEMBER

- Take turns talking and listening.
- Share your ideas.
- Explain your thinking.
- Show respect for others.

Work with your group to answer the questions. You will read your answers to the class.

1. What is the title of the book?

2. Who is the author?

3. Describe the main character.

4. What was one inference you were able to make?

5. What clues in the story helped you to make that inference?

6. What was one problem the characters had in the story?

7. What was the solution to the problem?

8. What was one thing that caused something else to happen?

Pick your role.

Leader	Recorder	Time Keeper	Helper	Motivator
Make sure students perform their roles.	Write down the answers.	Make sure your group finishes on time.	Gather materials. Ask teacher for help.	Encourage group members.

REMEMBER

- Take turns talking and listening.
- Share your ideas.
- Explain your thinking.
- Show respect for others.

Work with your group to answer the questions. You will read your answers to the class.

1. What is the title of the book?

2. Who is the author?

3. What is the book about?

4. What did you learn about this topic?

5. What did you know about this topic from your own life?

6. What else would you like to learn about this topic?

7. What generalizations did you make about this topic?

8. Summarize the events of the story in order.

BOOK TALKS

Pick your role.

Leader ☆	Recorder ✏	Time Keeper 🕐	Helper 📏	Motivator 👍
Make sure students perform their roles.	Write down the group's answers.	Make sure your group finishes on time.	Gather materials. Ask teacher for help.	Encourage group members.

REMEMBER

- Take turns talking and listening.
- Share your ideas.
- Explain your thinking.
- Show respect for others.

Work with your group to answer the questions. You will read your answers to the class.

1. What is the title of the book?
2. Who is the author?
3. Describe the main character.
4. What was a conclusion you made while reading the story?
5. What clues in the story helped you to draw that conclusion?
6. What was one problem the characters had in the story?
7. What was the solution to the problem?
8. What was one inference you made, and what clues helped you to make an inference?

Pick your role.

Leader	Recorder	Time Keeper	Helper	Motivator
Make sure students perform their roles.	Write down the answers.	Make sure your group finishes on time.	Gather materials. Ask teacher for help.	Encourage group members.

REMEMBER

- Take turns talking and listening.
- Share your ideas.
- Explain your thinking.
- Show respect for others.

Work with your group to answer the questions. You will read your answers to the class.

1. What is the title of the book?
2. Who is the author?
3. What is the book about?
4. What did you learn about this topic?
5. What did you know about this topic from your own life?
6. What else would you like to learn about this topic?
7. What was one thing that caused something else to happen?
8. Tell a short summary of the story.

Pick your role.

Leader	Recorder	Time Keeper	Helper	Motivator
Make sure students perform their roles.	Write down the group's answers.	Make sure your group finishes on time.	Gather materials. Ask teacher for help.	Encourage group members.

REMEMBER

- Take turns talking and listening.
- Share your ideas.
- Explain your thinking.
- Show respect for others.

Work with your group to answer the questions about the biography. You will read your answers to the class.

1. What is the title of the book?
2. Who is the author?
3. Tell about the person described in the biography.
4. What was one inference you were able to make?
5. What clues in the biography helped you to make that inference?
6. Summarize the biography.
7. Why did the author write the biography?
8. How do you think he or she feels about the person described in the biography?

Pick your role.

Leader ☆	Recorder ✏	Time Keeper 🕙	Helper 📏	Motivator 👍
Make sure students perform their roles.	Write down the answers.	Make sure your group finishes on time.	Gather materials. Ask teacher for help.	Encourage group members.

REMEMBER

- Take turns talking and listening.
- Share your ideas.
- Explain your thinking.
- Show respect for others.

Work with your group to answer the questions. You will read your answers to the class.

1. What is the title of the book?
2. Who is the author?
3. What is the book about?
4. What did you learn about this topic?
5. What did you know about this topic from your own life?
6. Compare and contrast two things in the story.
7. Tell three facts from the story.
8. Tell two opinions from the story.

Pick your role.

Leader	Recorder	Time Keeper	Helper	Motivator
Make sure students perform their roles.	Write down the group's answers.	Make sure your group finishes on time.	Gather materials. Ask teacher for help.	Encourage group members.

REMEMBER

- Take turns talking and listening.
- Share your ideas.
- Explain your thinking.
- Show respect for others.

Work with your group to answer the questions. You will read your answers to the class.

1. What is the title of the book?
2. Who is the author?
3. Describe the main character.
4. Think about what the characters did in the story. What judgments did you make about them because of their actions?
5. Compare and contrast two characters from the story.
6. Summarize the story.
7. Why did the author write the story?
8. How do you think he or she feels about the characters or plot of the story?

Pick your role.

Leader	Recorder	Time Keeper	Helper	Motivator
Make sure students perform their roles.	Write down the answers.	Make sure your group finishes on time.	Gather materials. Ask teacher for help.	Encourage group members.

REMEMBER

- Take turns talking and listening.
- Share your ideas.
- Explain your thinking.
- Show respect for others.

Work with your group to answer the questions. You will read your answers to the class.

1. What is the title of the book?

2. Who is the author?

3. What is the book about?

4. What did you learn about this topic?

5. What did you know about this topic from your own life?

6. Compare and contrast two things in the story.

7. What words or sentences did the author use to persuade you of his or her opinion on the topic?

8. Summarize the events of the story.

Pick your role.

Leader ☆	Recorder ✏	Time Keeper 🕐	Helper 📏	Motivator 👍
Make sure students perform their roles.	Write down the group's answers.	Make sure your group finishes on time.	Gather materials. Ask teacher for help.	Encourage group members.

REMEMBER

- Take turns talking and listening.
- Share your ideas.
- Explain your thinking.
- Show respect for others.

Work with your group to answer the questions. You will read your answers to the class.

1. What is the title of the book?
2. Who is the author?
3. Describe the main character.
4. What questions did you have while reading the story?
5. Describe the events of the story in order.
6. What was the theme of the story?
7. What conclusions did you draw while reading, and what clues helped you?
8. Compare and contrast two important events in the story.

© Macmillan/McGraw-Hill

Pick your role.

Leader ⭐	Recorder ✏️	Time Keeper 🕐	Helper 📏	Motivator 👍
Make sure students perform their roles.	Write down the answers.	Make sure your group finishes on time.	Gather materials. Ask teacher for help.	Encourage group members.

REMEMBER

- Take turns talking and listening.
- Share your ideas.
- Explain your thinking.
- Show respect for others.

Work with your group to answer the questions. You will read your answers to the class.

1. What is the title of the book?
2. Who is the author?
3. What is the book about?
4. What did you learn about this topic?
5. What did you know about this topic from your own life?
6. Tell how two things mentioned in the story are alike and different.
7. Talk about one generalization you can make about something in the story.
8. What was one problem and one solution in the story?

Name _____ Date _____

Write some new words you learned below.

1.
2.
3.
4.
5.

6.
7.
8.
9.
10.

Now I am a better

☐ reader
☐ writer
☐ listener
☐ speaker

because

_____

_____

_____

_____

I want to get better at

☐ reading
☐ writing
☐ listening
☐ speaking

because

_____

_____

_____

_____

In order to get better, I will _____

_____

_____

Name _____ Date _____

Group Members

Write the names of the students giving the presentation.

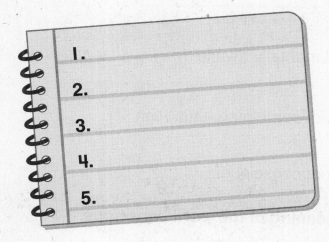

1.
2.
3.
4.
5.

My classmates did this well

☐ spoke clearly

☐ read clearly

☐ addressed the class

☐ showed they were prepared

☐ motivated their group members

My favorite part of the presentation was

_____

_____

_____

_____

My classmates can try this next time:

_____

_____

_____

_____

© Macmillan/McGraw-Hill

Name _____

Vocabulary: Dictionary/Multiple-Meaning Words

• A **multiple meaning word** has more than one meaning.

Write the number of the correct meaning of *conscious* for each sentence.

| conscious | 1. to be aware |
| | 2. to be physically and mentally awake |

1. ___*1*___ Rachel was conscious of something hitting the window repeatedly.

2. ___*2*___ The injured man was not conscious.

Write your own sentence using one meaning of the word *conscious*.

3. ___Answers will vary.___

Phonics: Short Vowels with Varient Spellings

The words *bank, pen, pig, dog,* and *mug* have a short vowel sound.

  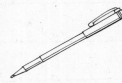

bank　　　**pen**　　　**pig**　　　**dog**　　　**mug**

Write each word in the chart under its short vowel sound.

| prank | shop | next | clash | drill |
| threat | shrunk | tough | rhythm | clock |

short *a*	short *e*	short *i*	short *o*	short *u*
prank	next	drill	shop	shrunk
clash	threat	rhythm	clock	tough

Name _____

Comprehension: Analyze Character, Setting, and Plot

Think about the characters, setting, and plot events in *The Rescue Team*. Circle the answer that completes each sentence. Write *setting*, *character*, or *plot* on the line to tell what each question is about.

1. Rachel likes her horse, Lucky, and

   a. cooking   **(b.)** biology   _character_

2. Scratch was found

   a. dripping wet   **(b.)** covered with   _plot_
   mud and oil

3. Rachel lives in the state of

   a. Nevada   **(b.)** California   _setting_

4. Write a sentence that describes the setting of this story in greater detail.

   Possible answer: The setting is rural. There are

   gardens and fields near Rachel's house.

Grammar: Sentence Types and Fragments

• An **interrogative sentence** asks a question.
• An **exclamatory sentence** expresses a strong feeling.

Write *I* if the sentence is interrogative. Write *E* if the sentence is exclamatory.

1. ____I____ Have you seen this shell?

2. ____I____ Is Carrie on the boat?

3. ____E____ It is so pretty!

Vocabulary: Dictionary/Multiple-Meaning Words

Read the definitions below. Write the multiple-meaning word that matches the definition.

conscious	rose	rock

1. a type of flower ___rose___

2. to be aware of something ___conscious___

3. to sway back and forth ___rock___

4. to be awake ___conscious___

5. the past tense of *rise* ___rose___

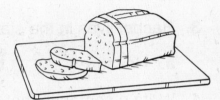

Phonics: Short Vowels with Variant Spellings

Circle the word that has the same vowel sound as the underlined word.

1. <u>thread</u>   (bread)   move   real

2. <u>rim</u>   rhyme   (myth)   mind

3. <u>shove</u>   more   roll   (tough)

4. <u>rhythm</u>   mile   brook   (strict)

5. <u>dread</u>   (threat)   plaid   tea

Write a sentence. Use one of the answers from above.

6. ___Answers will vary.___

Comprehension: Analyze Character, Setting, and Plot
Read the sentences. Decide if they are details that tell about a character, setting, or story's plot and write the answer.

1. A firefighter's job is to locate people who are trapped in burning buildings

   and to put out dangerous fires. _____Character_____

2. Emergency vehicles make many trips from the hospital into the city each day. Inside every emergency vehicle there needs to be medical supplies and a cot for patients.

   _____Setting_____

3. The swimming pool was very crowded. A swimmer was having troubles.

   The lifeguard jumped in the pool. _____Plot_____

Grammar: Sentence Types and Fragments
Label the sentence types below. Then rewrite each sentence to change it into the sentence type in parentheses.

1. _____declarative_____ I hit a home run. (change to exclamatory)

   I hit a home run!
   _____

2. _____fragment_____ packed the car. (change to a complete sentence)

   We packed the car.
   _____

3. _____interrogative_____ Why are plants green? (change to declarative)

   Plants are green.
   _____

4. _____declarative_____ I want you to stay here. (change to imperative)

   Stay here!
   _____

Name _____

Vocabulary: Word Parts/Compound Words
- A **compound word** is formed from two or more words put together, such as *undergrowth*.

Write the words together to form a compound word. Then use the compound words to complete the sentences.

1. back   pack   *backpack* _____

2. earth   quake   *earthquake* _____

3. The ground shakes in an *earthquake* _____.

4. When I get to school I put my *backpack* _____ in a locker.

Phonics: Long Vowels
The words *cave*, *bean*, *slope*, *line*, and *fuse* have long vowel sounds.

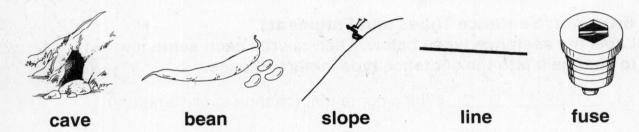

cave   **bean**   **slope**   **line**   **fuse**

Write the words in the chart under their long vowel sound.

boat	bathe	queen	home	train
reach	light	cue	fly	new

long *a*	long *e*	long *i*	long *o*	long *u*
bathe	*queen*	*light*	*boat*	*cue*
train	*reach*	*fly*	*home*	*new*

Name _____

Comprehension: Analyze Character, Setting, and Plot
Read the statements about the characters, setting, and plot in
A Great Discovery. Choose the detail that supports each statement.

1. Character: Sir Leonard Woolley is friendly.

   (a.) He greets Abdullah in Arabic.

   b. He waves to tourists in Baghdad.

2. Plot: Abdullah has a problem.

   a. He has broken a valuable artifact.

   (b.) He found gold beads, but he does not know whether to show them to the others.

3. Setting: The story takes place at a remote, or distant, excavation site.

   a. The characters are trying to solve a murder mystery.

   (b.) The characters are exploring ancient Sumerian graves.

4. Plot: Sir Leonard Woolley rewards Abdullah.

   a. Abdullah paid for his discovery, just like the other workers.

   (b.) Abdullah is invited to learn more about archeology and asked to clean pottery instead of digging.

Grammar: Subjects and Predicates
- The **subject** of a sentence tells who or what the sentence is about.
- The **predicate** of a sentence tells what the subject does.

Underline each subject. Circle each predicate.

1. Abdullah worked on a dig.

2. They looked for a tomb.

3. He found gold beads.

4. The interpreter spoke two languages.

Write a sentence. Underline the subject and circle the predicate.

5. Answers will vary. _____

Name _____

Vocabulary: Word Parts/Compound Words

Read the compound words below. Write the two smaller words that make up the compound word on the lines.

1. undergrowth   _under_   +   _growth_
2. foretold   _fore_   +   _told_
3. withstood   _with_   +   _stood_
4. headscarf   _head_   +   _scarf_
5. sunrise   _sun_   +   _rise_

Phonics: Long Vowels

Circle the word that does not have the same long vowel sound as the underlined word.

1. <u>rain</u>   name   (cat)   quaint

2. <u>keen</u>   bleach   theme   (red)

3. <u>loan</u>   (slop)   coax   foe

4. <u>why</u>   nylon   tile   (till)

5. <u>league</u>   bleak   meek   (plague)

Write a sentence. Use one of the long vowel words from above.

6. _____

_____

_____

Name _____

Comprehension: Analyze Character, Setting, and Plot
Read the paragraph below. Then, answer questions about the characters, setting, and problem.

Professor Bingham wanted to go on an adventure. In the country of Peru in South America, he hoped to make a new discovery. The lost city of the Inca Empire was somewhere at the top of the mountain. With his students, he set out on a long hike in the Andes Mountain range. The students and Professor Bingham had a difficult time climbing 8,000 feet above the ground. The air was thin and everyone had difficulty breathing. One student became very sick. When they reached the top, their dream was realized. Before them was the ancient city of Machu Picchu.

1. Where is the city of Machu Picchu?

   At the top of a mountain in the Andes
   Mountains in the country of Peru.

2. What was one problem in this story?

   Possible answer: It was very difficult to climb and

   breathe 8,000 feet above ground. One student

   became sick.

3. Describe Professor Bingham.

   He likes an adventure and had a goal that he

   accomplished.

Grammar: Subjects and Predicates
Write two sentences about the picture.
Underline each subject and circle each predicate.

1. The boy and girl are digging.

2. Possible answer: A garden is fun to work in.

Name _____

Vocabulary: Context Clues/Definitions

• **Context clues** help describe unfamiliar words in a sentence.

Read the paragraph. Use context clues to define the words that appear in the story.

    A helicopter is different from other flying machines in several ways. You can see the blades turning on a helicopter. The blades are large, flat pieces of metal that rotate on top of the helicopter. They are part of its main rotor.

1. flying machine _Possible answer: piece of equipment such as a helicopter or a jet plane_

2. blade _Possible answer: large, flat pieces of metal that rotate on top of the helicopter_

Write a sentence using one of the words from above.

3. _Answers will vary._ _____

Phonics: Words with *ei* and *ie*

Words with *ei* often have the long *a* sound. Words with *ie* often have the long *e* sound.

shield

Read the sentences aloud and underline the words with long e spelled *ie* and long a spelled *ei*.

1. We grow crops in the field.

2. Our neighbors are very friendly.

3. I had a big piece of birthday cake.

Name _____

Comprehension: Identify Main Idea and Details
- The **main idea** is the most important idea or theme of a topic.
- **Details** are supporting facts.

Select two details from *Learning to Fly from Nature* that give information about each main idea.

Main Idea

1. ___c, e___ People studied the dragonfly's ability to fly in many directions.

2. ___a, d___ Bats use echolocation to fly in the dark and hunt for food.

3. ___b, f___ People have copied how a bird glides.

Details

a. Sound waves help bats find food.

b. Hang gliders ride or glide on currents of air like some birds.

c. The helicopter has wings called rotors that are similar to dragonfly wings.

d. Radar is a form of echolocation that uses radio waves.

e. The dragonfly has two pair of wings.

f. A plane is different from a bird because it can only glide without an engine for a short time.

Grammar: Conjunctions and Compound Sentences
- A **compound sentence** is two or more sentences joined by a conjunction, such as *or*, *and*, or *but*.

Write the pairs of sentences as compound sentences.

1. Most birds cannot fly backward. Hummingbirds can.

   Most birds cannot fly backward, but hummingbirds can.

2. Bees make honey. They store it in their hive.

   Bees make honey, and they store it in their hive.

Vocabulary: Context Clues/Definitions

Read the sentences below. Fill in the correct word using the definition in the sentence as a context clue.

concentrated	absorb	altered	seized

1. He __concentrated__, or focused really hard, on studying for the test.

2. A sponge will soak up, or __absorb__, what was spilled.

3. She __seized__, or grabbed, the flag to win the game.

4. He __altered__, or changed, the way he usually dressed.

Phonics: Words with *ei* and *ie*

Read the words in the word bank. List each word under the column long *a* or long *e*.

yield	piece	rein
sleigh	eight	shield

long *a*	long *e*
eight	yield
rein	piece
sleigh	shield

Write a sentence. Use a word with the long *a* sound or the long *e* sound from the activity above.

Answers will vary.
_____

© Macmillan/McGraw-Hill

Comprehension: Identify Main Idea and Details
Read the paragraph below. Then, answer the questions about the paragraph's main idea and details.

Science and the Mosquito

Mosquitoes have many ways to find people to bite. Over the last 30 million years, the mosquito has perfected its ability to find humans. Mosquitoes can sense carbon dioxide from a person's breath up to 100 feet away. Chemicals found in sweat can also attract mosquitoes to humans. Clothing that looks different than the natural background draws mosquitoes close and mosquitoes can also detect body heat. All of these factors lead a mosquito to bite your arms, legs, and ankles.

1. Which sentence tells the main idea in this paragraph?
   the first sentence

2. Write three details that support the main idea: Answers will vary.

   a. Mosquitoes sense carbon dioxide up to 100 feet away.

   b. Human sweat attracts mosquitoes.

   c. Clothing that stands out attracts mosquitoes to people.

Grammar: Conjunctions and Compound Sentences
Write three compound sentences. Use *and*, *or*, and *but*.

Answers will vary.

Possible answers: She grows

1. and flowers, and she grows vegetables.

2. but The dog plays, but the cat sleeps.

3. or She has to water her flowers, or they will not grow.

Vocabulary: Context Clues/Restatement

- A **restatement** is a word or phrase that describes something in the sentence.

Read the sentences. Circle the words and phrases that restate the underlined words. Use these words as context clues.

1. The area known as the Four Corners is <u>arid</u>, or dry, because it's a desert.

2. The United States Government and the Navajo people signed a <u>treaty</u>. This agreement gave the Navajo People land in the Four Corners.

3. <u>Dawn</u> is the time of day when the sun rises.

4. When people can't grow food, there is <u>famine</u>, or hunger.

5. Lamb's wool that is <u>sheared</u>, or cut off, is called fleece.

Phonics: *r*-Controlled Vowels

The words *reward* and *thorn* have *r*-controlled vowels.

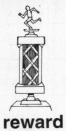

reward

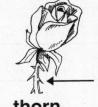

thorn

Write each word in the column under its *r*-controlled vowel sound.

| search | mourn | thorn | sparkle | chart |
| earnest | torch | court | burnt | fur |

ar	*ear*	*ou*	*or*	*ur*
sparkle	search	court	torch	fur
chart	earnest	mourn	thorn	burnt

Name _____

Comprehension: Identify Cause and Effect
- A **cause** is the reason for an action.
- An **effect** is the result of an action.

Write the letter of each cause next to its effect.

Cause

1. _____b_____ The United States and the Navajos signed a treaty in 1868.

2. _____a_____ Showing generosity, Spider Woman rescued a boy and taught him how to weave.

3. _____c_____ Spanish settlers brought Churro sheep.

Effect

a. The Navajo people learned how to weave.

b. The Navajo were given their own government called the Navajo Nation.

c. The fleece of Churro sheep are used by Navajo weavers to create beautiful rugs.

Grammar: Clauses and Complex Sentences
- A **complex sentence** contains at least one main clause and one subordinate clause.
- A **main clause** can stand alone.
- A **subordinate clause** cannot.

Underline each main clause. Circle each subordinate clause.

1. When the weather was good, the Navajo planted corn, squash, and melons.

2. When the weather was bad, there was a famine.

3. If Navajo children are bad, Spider Woman will eat them.

Write a complex sentence of your own. Use the picture.

4. Answers will vary.
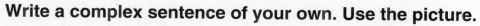

Name _____

Vocabulary: Context Clues/Restatement
Read the following sentences. Use the restatement in the sentence as a context clue to choose a word that fits.

famine	sphere	ricocheted	undetected	generosity

1. The ____famine____, or widespread lack of food, left them helpless.

2. Her ____generosity____, or giving nature, makes her a great friend.

3. The fierce animal was ____undetected____, or was not noticed, by its prey.

4. The ball ____ricocheted____, or bounced off at an angle, from the tennis court fence.

5. The object was a ____sphere____, or the shape of a ball.

Phonics: *r*-Controlled Vowels
Read the underlined word aloud. Circle the word that has the same *r*-controlled vowel sound as the underlined word.

1. lair   (stair)   scar   star

2. hear   heart   (veer)   hair

3. fierce   pair   (pierce)   barn

4. scorn   (mourn)   fire   fern

5. surf   door   wharf   (burnt)

Write a sentence. Use one of the *r*-controlled vowel words from above.

6. Answers will vary. _____

Name _____

Comprehension: Identify Cause and Effect

Read each cause on the left side of the page. Choose the letter of the effect that matches it. Use information about your family to complete the cause and effect in the last item.

Cause

1. ___a___ My mother is a piano teacher.

2. ___c___ My grandfather owned a restaurant.

3. ___b___ My older brother always included me in the neighborhood baseball games.

4. My family _was 100% Italian and my grandmother passed on her recipe for spaghetti sauce._

Effect

a. I learned to play the piano as a very young child.

b. My favorite sport is baseball.

c. My father is an excellent cook.

d. _Possible answer: In my family we always make homemade spaghetti sauce._

Students should write a cause that connects to the completed effect in letter d.

Explode

Grammar: Clauses and Complex Sentences

Form a complex sentence by combining the clauses. Write the new sentence on the line. Then underline the independent clause and circle the dependent clause.

1. Because it was the Fourth of July. We watched the fireworks.

   (Because it was the Fourth of July) we watched the fireworks.

2. The elders showed great generosity. Because it was the Chinese New Year's Day.

   The elders showed great generosity (because it was the Chinese New Year's Day.)

Name _____

Vocabulary: Analogy/Antonyms

• **Antonyms** are words with opposite meanings.

Choose words from the word bank to complete the following analogies.

| microscopic | unnecessary | protect | waste |

1. sink is to float as endanger is to __protect__

2. short is to tall as conserve is to __waste__

3. exciting is to boring as vital is to __unnecessary__

4. fast is to slow as huge is to __microscopic__

Write a sentence using two words that are antonyms.

5. __Answers will vary.__ _____

Phonics: Compound Words

• **Compound words** can be joined together, hyphenated, or separated.

Write each compound word in the appropriate column.

| fingernail | twenty-five | brother-in-law | science fiction |
| after-school | light bulb | seashell | watermelon | field trip |

joined	hyphenated	separated
fingernail	twenty-five	field trip
seashell	brother-in-law	science fiction
watermelon	after-school	light bulb

Comprehension: Identify Main Idea and Details

Read the three main ideas from *The King of Birds*. Write the letter of the main idea next to the appropriate detail.

Main Ideas

A. The peregrine falcon is a bird of prey.

B. DDT caused a lot of damage in the natural world.

C. Falcons migrate south when the seasons change.

Details

1. ____A____ The falcon has a curved beak that helps to tear the flesh of its prey.

2. ____B____ After falcons ate insects that had DDT in their bodies, falcon eggs were thin and broke easily.

3. ____C____ Other birds that migrate at the change of the seasons become the falcons' prey.

4. ____A____ The falcon has a special tooth on its beak that breaks the back of its prey.

Grammar: Run-on Sentences

• A **run-on sentence** joins two or more sentences with no punctuation.

Write the run-on sentences as separate sentences.

1. DDT is a poison it kills bugs.

    DDT is a poison. It kills bugs. _____

2. Some birds are dehydrated they need water.

    Some birds are dehydrated. They need water. _____

3. We must conserve wildlife it will be all gone.

    We must conserve wildlife. It will be all gone. _____

Vocabulary: Analogy/Antonyms

Read the underlined words below. Match the word with its antonym.

1. <u>tall</u> ___b___   **a.** waste

2. <u>conserve</u> ___a___   **b.** short

3. <u>vital</u> ___d___   **c.** smooth

4. <u>dehydrated</u> ___e___   **d.** unimportant

5. <u>rough</u> ___c___   **e.** soaked

Phonics: Compound Words

Read the words on the left. Draw a line between the
two smaller words that make up the compound word.
Then write the definition of the compound word.
Use the smaller words as clues.

Words	Meaning
1. down|pour	when the rain pours down hard
2. apple|sauce	a sauce made from apples
3. flash|bulb	a bulb used for a flash when taking pictures.
4. head|ache	a head pain
5. hail|storm	a storm with hail

Write a sentence. Use one of the compound words from above.

6. Answers will vary. _____

Comprehension: Identify Main Idea and Details
Read the main idea. Place a check mark next to each detail that tells more about the main idea.

> **Main Idea:** The Giant Panda is one of the most endangered species in the world.

Details

√ _____ The current panda population around the world includes only 1,000 pandas.

_____ It was once thought that pandas were part of the raccoon family.

√ _____ Without enough bamboo to eat, pandas can starve.

√ _____ Very few panda cubs are born each year because a female panda has the chance to become pregnant only one or two times within a year.

Grammar: Run-on Sentences
Read the sentences below. If the sentence is complete, write C on the line. If the sentence is a run-on sentence, write R on the line.

1. __R__ The couple gave water to the dehydrated stray cat the cat needed a home.

2. __R__ He ran up the hill she followed him there.

3. __C__ They grew to love the animals that they cared for.

4. __C__ Anwar could not decide if he wanted to go.

Choose one of the run-on sentences from above. Rewrite it so that it is two complete sentences.

5. Answers will vary. _____

Vocabulary A **compound word** is two words joined to form
a new word with a new meaning.

undergrowth   applesauce   withstood   foretold   newspaper

Phonics An *r*-controlled vowel, or vowel that appears before the
letter *r*, usually does not have a short or long vowel sound. The
r sound changes the vowel sound to a different sound.

Words with *r*-Controlled Vowels

herself   fierce   torch   storm   star   carve

Comprehension Elements of a story include the **characters**, **plot**,
and **setting**. The characters in a story are the people and animals.
The plot is the events that happen in the story. The setting tells when
and where the story takes place.

The Rescue Team: Chapter One

Events in a Plot	Rachel is riding Lucky through the field.	Rachel hears Scratch barking and tries to find him.
Characters	Rachel	Lucky
Settings	California hills	The creek

Grammar A **declarative sentence** makes a statement.
An **interrogative sentence** asks a question. An **exclamatory
sentence** expresses strong feeling. A sentence **fragment** is a group
of words that do not express a complete thought. A **run-on sentence**
is two or more sentences written together.

Declarative   Babe Ruth was a great baseball player.
Interrogative   Would you please wash the dishes?
Exclamatory   That was the best movie I've ever seen!
Fragment   Sam in the car.
Run-on   I am hungry I want a sandwich.

Name _____

**Next to each vocabulary word, write the letter of its meaning.
Then circle the vocabulary words that have an *r*-controlled vowel.**

1. (procedure) __d__

2. foretold __a__

3. (conserve) __c__

4. withstood __b__

a. predicted

b. endured

c. save

d. process

**Write the correct punctuation where it belongs
in the story. Circle the sentence fragments and
underline run-on sentences.**

Hotshots and Smoke Jumpers

5. When people are careless while camping or when a summer
   has been too hot and

6. dry__,__ wildfires are more likely to occur. Outdoor fires require special
   teams of

7. experienced firefighters such as Hotshots and Smoke Jumpers__T__ they
   are trained in the

8. outdoors. Hotshots fight the toughest part of a fire and use specialized
   hand tools,

9. including chainsaws and fire line explosives. Smokejumpers are
   firefighters

10. that parachute from planes. (To attack wild land fires in remote areas.)

11. Could you do this job__?__ Not me__!__.

12. What is the main idea in the text?
    Outdoor fires require special teams of firefighters.
    _____

    _____

Phonics: Short and Long Vowels; *r*-Controlled Vowels

Read the paragraphs. In the first paragraph, circle words that
have long vowel sounds. In the second paragraph, underline
the *r*-controlled vowels.

Emergency Response Team

Oil and toxic chemicals are transported to their
destinations on barges, trucks, and (trains). Accidents
can happen with hazardous materials. A spill can
create an environmental disaster. Then the Emergency
Response (Team) (leads) the (clean-up) work.

The Emergency Response Team plans the work
that needs to be done. They get rid of oil and chemical
spills. They also remove pollutants and contaminants.
These teams are the experts.

Comprehension: Main Idea and Details

1. Write a sentence that tells the main idea of this text. Then write a detail
    that supports the main idea.

    The Emergency Response Team cleans up

    environmental disasters. They clean up oil and

    chemical spills.

2. Draw and complete a Main Idea and Details graphic organizer for
    this text.

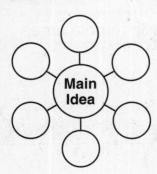

Main Idea—Emergency Response
Team cleans up environmental
disasters. Details—removes
pollutants, cleans up oil and
chemical spills

Vocabulary
Read each sentence. Circle the letter of the word that best completes the sentence.

1. Two cars crashed in the _____ of 1st Avenue and Clark Street.
   - **a.** intersection
   - **b.** lane
   - **c.** curb
   - **d.** construction

2. The children used sponges and rags to _____ the milk they spilled.
   - **a.** leak
   - **b.** pour
   - **c.** drench
   - **d.** absorb

3. Donato threw a ball indoors, and it _____ off the wall and flew into a picture frame, which broke.
   - **a.** fell
   - **b.** slid
   - **c.** ricocheted
   - **d.** dribbled

Match the parts of compound words. Draw a line from the word on the right to the one on the left that completes the compound word.

4. with   **a.** growth
5. fore   **b.** stood
6. under   **c.** told

Phonics: *r*-Controlled Vowels
Circle the word that has an *r*-controlled vowel in each group.

7. reply   train   fierce

8. carve   ripe   green

Grammar: Sentence Combining, Clauses and Complex Sentences; Conjunctions and Compound Sentences

Circle the independent clause in each sentence.

1. When the weather was good, the Navajo planted corn, squash, and melons.

2. If the soccer team plays well, they will win.

Complete each dependent clause to make a complex sentence.

3. _____ after a boy climbed to the top of Spider Rock.

   a. The Navajo learned how to weave

   b. Since the Navajo learned how

4. When the venomous snake bit Carlos, _____.

   a. of the desert

   b. he ran quickly for help.

The pairs of sentences have been combined to make compound sentences. Circle the letter of the sentence that uses the best conjunction.

5. Some animals in captivity are dangerous. Some are harmless.

   a. Some animals in captivity are dangerous, or some are harmless.

   b. Some animals in captivity are dangerous, but some are harmless.

6. We stopped at the intersection. We bought a souvenir from a vendor.

   a. We stopped at the intersection, and we bought a souvenir from a vendor.

   b. We stopped at the intersection, or we bought a souvenir from a vendor.

7. We must protect our wildlife. Many species will become extinct.

   a. We must protect our wildlife, or many species will become extinct.

   b. We must protect our wildlife, but many species will become extinct.

Name _____

Editing: Sentence Fragments, Run-on Sentences, and Punctuation

Read the story. Find errors with run-on sentences, sentence fragments, and commas. Circle the errors and write the corrections on the lines.

When the Ventura brothers, Pablo and Luis, went to Alaska for their winter vacation everyone wondered why they would choose such a cold place. They had a good reason. They went to photograph a bird. The American Bald Eagle. Their local newspaper back home was offering prize money for the best picture of this famous national bird. The brothers were excited the Chilkat River near Haines, Alaska, has a salmon run that attracts around 4,000 bald eagles each year! The 200,000 to 500,000 salmon are easy prey. For the eagles to catch. When the brothers returned home they developed their twenty rolls of film chose their favorite picture, and won the prize.

1. vacation,

2. bird, the

3. excited. The

4. prey for

5. home,

6. film,

Comprehension: Character, Plot, and Setting, Cause and Effect

1. Who are the characters? What is the plot? What is the setting?

Characters—Pablo and Luis Plot—Two brothers go to Alaska to photograph the bald eagle to win a contest. Setting—the outdoors, Alaska

2. Why did so many bald eagles go to the Chilkat River in Alaska?

to eat the thousands of salmon that go there

Name _____

Vocabulary: Word Parts/Inflectional Endings

- An **inflectional ending** at the end of a verb changes its meaning. Adding **-ed** to the end of a verb shows it is in the past tense.

Circle all the verbs in the sentences. Then underline verbs with inflectional endings.

1. Jenna and her family (moved) last summer.

2. Jenna will (try out) for the basketball team at her school.

3. Jenna (was) happy when she (learned) that she (had made) the team.

4. (Look) at the envelope to (see) where the letter (was postmarked).

5. They (relaxed) during their vacation.

Phonics: Plurals

- The **plural** form of a word usually ends in **s** and shows there is more than one of something.

Some nouns below are singular and some are plural. Say them out loud. Write the singular nouns in the singular nouns column. Write the plural nouns in the plural nouns column.

| halves | sister | data | potato |
| photos | trophies | postmark | shelf |

Singular Nouns	Plural Nouns
sister	halves
potato	data
shelf	photos
postmark	trophies

© Macmillan/McGraw-Hill

Name _____

Comprehension: Make Inferences

- An **inference** is a conclusion based on what you already know and what you have read.

Read each detail from the story. Then, finish writing the inference for each story detail.

1. Jenna sighed as she thought about how her new school was three times bigger than her old school.

   Inference: Jenna feels _Possible Answer: nervous or anxious_ _____ about going to a much bigger school.

2. At dinner, Jenna's parents look at each other and have worried faces.

   Inference: Jenna's parents think that _Possible Answer: Jenna had a bad day._ _____

3. Gina, Jenna's former coach, sent her a letter postmarked from Jenna's old town.

   Inference: Even though Jenna has moved, Gina _Possible Answer: still cares about Jenna and wants to encourage her._ _____

Grammar: Common and Proper Nouns

- A **common noun** names a person, place, thing, or idea.
- A **proper noun** names a specific person, place, thing, or idea and is always capitalized.

Write on the lines whether each underlined noun is common or proper.

1. Sean was grouchy because he was tired. _____ proper _____

2. The Wildcats won. _____ proper _____

3. The pennant was orange and white. _____ common _____

Write a sentence using a common and a proper noun.

Answers will vary.
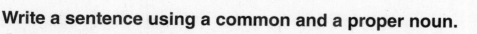

Name _____

Vocabulary: Word Parts/Inflectional Endings
Read the words below. Rewrite each word with the endings *-ed* and *-ing*.

1. postmark __postmarked,__ __postmarking__
2. enthrall __enthralled,__ __enthralling__
3. rent __rented,__ __renting__
4. talk __talked,__ __talking__

Write two sentences. Use two of the answers from above.

5. __Answers will vary.__ _____
6. __Answers will vary.__ _____

Phonics: Plurals
Read the words below. Write their plural forms on the lines.

1. piano __pianos__
2. butterfly __butterflies__
3. hero __heroes__
4. child __children__
5. scarf __scarves__

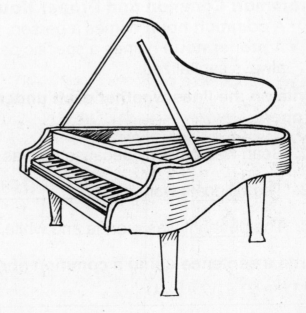

Name _____

Comprehension: Make Inferences
Place a check mark in front of each sentence that makes a good inference about the information in the paragraph.

At the 1988 Olympics, speed skater Dan Jansen was expected to take home two gold medals. Only hours before the 500-meter race, Dan's sister, Jane, died from leukemia. That day Dan stumbled rounding a corner and was disqualified from the race. In 1992, Dan only placed fourth and then twenty-sixth. The 1994 Olympic games were the last chance for Jansen. Dan finished the first race in eighth place. But he finished the final race in first place, earned a gold medal, and set a world record. Dan Jansen celebrated by taking a victory lap, while holding his baby daughter, Jane. Today we remember Dan's strong sense of determination.

1. Which sentences make a logical inference?

a. _____✓_____ Dan did not skate well in 1988 because he was so upset about his sister's death.

b. _____✓_____ After the 1988 and the 1992 Olympics, critics didn't think Jansen was a potential gold medalist.

c. _____ Jansen did not train well for the 1988 and 1992 Olympics.

Grammar: Common and Proper Nouns
Rewrite each sentence. Capitalize the proper nouns and underline each common noun.

1. sam went to a baseball game today.
   Sam went to a baseball game today.
   _____

2. The teams playing were the cubs and the white sox.
   The teams playing were the Cubs and the
   _____
   White Sox.
   _____

Name _____

Vocabulary: Dictionary/Pronunciation Key
- A dictionary has **pronunciation keys** to tell how to pronounce words.

Say the words *astride* and *astronomer* out loud. Then answer the questions.

> **astride** (ə strīde´) with legs apart or on each side
> **astronomer** (ə stron´ ə mer) person who observes and studies stars, planets and other objects in the sky

1. How many syllables does the word *astride* have? _____two_____

2. How many syllables does the word *astronomer* have? _____four_____

3. Which syllable is stressed in the word *astronomer*? ___the second one___

4. Are the *a* in *astride* and the *a* in *astronomer* pronounced the same way? _____yes_____

Phonics: Inflected Endings Adding *-ed, -ing*
- Verbs that end in *-ed* show something happened in the past.
- Verbs that end in *-ing* show that something is happening now.

Write the *-ed* and *-ing* forms of the verbs on the lines in the chart.

Verb	*-ed* form	*-ing* form
accuse	accused	accusing
marvel	marveled	marveling
patrol	patrolled	patrolling
encourage	encouraged	encouraging
orbit	orbited	orbiting

Name _____

Comprehension: Make Inferences
• An **inference** is a conclusion based on information from the author and the reader's previous knowledge.

Read the details from *Ancient Astronomers*. Then, write an inference.

1. **Detail:** Mound Builders built enormous mounds in the shapes of many animals. Scientists think the mounds represent stars or constellations.

   What inference can you make about the Mound Builders' connection to nature? _Possible Answer: They had a strong connection to nature and observed nature closely._

2. **Detail:** The Anasazi people built a sun temple with windows that faced the direction of the setting and rising sun.

   What inference can you make about the Anasazi people and the sun? _Possible Answer: They thought that sunrise and sunset were important times of the day when special ceremonies should take place._

Grammar: Singular and Plural Nouns
• A **plural noun** names more than one person, place, or thing.

Write the plural form of each singular noun in parentheses (). If the noun ends in a consonant and *y*, change the *y* to *i* and add *-es*.

1. (Camera) broadcast pictures back to Earth. _Cameras_

2. There are many (galaxy) in the universe. _galaxies_

Use one of the plural nouns from above in a sentence of your own.

3. _Answers will vary._

Name _____

Vocabulary: Dictionary/Pronunciation Key

Read the pronunciation key. Then read the pronunciations for the words below. Answer the questions.

Pronunciation Key

a	hat	ī	ice
ā	āge	o	hot
e	let	ô	order
ē	equal	ō	ōpen
i	it	ə	takən

Pronunciations

broadcast (brôd′ kast′)
spicy \spī′sē\
vigil \vij′əl\

1. Does *vigil* have a long *i* sound in it? _____ no _____

2. What long vowel sounds are in *spicy*? _____ long *i* and long *e* _____

3. What word has the same sound as the second *a* in *broadcast*?

_____ hat _____

Phonics: Inflected Endings Adding -ed and -ing

Add -*ed* and -*ing* to the words below. Write the new words on the line.

1. travel ___ traveled ___ ___ traveling ___

2. wander ___ wandered ___ ___ wandering ___

3. marvel ___ marveled ___ ___ marveling ___

Comprehension: Make Inferences

Read the paragraph below. Then, read the details from the paragraph. Write the letters of two inferences that can be made from each detail.

The differences in the hours of sunlight help to create the seasons. In the Northern Hemisphere, the month of June is part of the season of summer. June 21 has the most hours of sunlight. This day is called the summer solstice. On that day, sunrise is the earliest, and sunset is the latest that it will be all year. The shortest day of the year, in the Northern Hemisphere, will take place six months later on December 21. This is called the winter solstice.

Detail: June 21 is the day with the most hours of sunlight in the Northern Hemisphere.

1. ____a____   2. ____d____

Detail: December 21 has the fewest hours of sunlight in the Northern Hemisphere.

3. ____b____   4. ____c____

Inferences

a. People can play sports and outdoor games for a longer time.

b. It will be dark when families are eating dinner.

c. Sunset will happen earlier, and the temperature will be colder.

d. The temperature is high because of the many hours of sunlight.

Grammar: Singular and Plural Nouns

Rewrite each sentence. Use the plural form of the word in ().

1. My (cousin) are coming to visit the space museum.

   My cousins are coming to visit the space museum.

2. They will stay for three (day).

   They will stay for three days.

Name _____

Vocabulary: Context Clues/Within a Paragraph

- **Context clues** are words that can help you figure out what other words mean.

Underline the context clues in the paragraph for the words below.

calamity	evacuate	shelters

A city or town that gets flooded goes through a calamity. This is a situation that makes life difficult and causes people to suffer. People have to evacuate their homes. They leave hoping to return soon and to find that they didn't lose much. Many people are taken to temporary housing for protection. They stay in these shelters until it's safe to return home.

Describe one word from the word bank.

1. _Answers will vary._ _____

Phonics: Words with /ô/, /ou/, /oi/, /oo/

Write each word from the word bank in the column according to its vowel sound.

v<u>au</u>lt

sl<u>ou</u>ch

s<u>oo</u>ty

gloom	fault	mound

au	ou	oo
fault	mound	gloom

© Macmillan/McGraw-Hill

Name _____

Comprehension: Make Generalizations

- A **generalization** is a statement in broad terms. It tells what a group of things or people have in common. A generalization statement may have one of these words: *most, always, never.*

Read the information from *The Flood of 1993*. Then, finish writing the generalization.

1. The Federal Emergency Management Agency, or FEMA, found shelter for people, made repairs, and gave insurance money.

    All federal agencies are good sources for

    Possible Answer: help during a disaster
    _____

2. More than 5,000 people used the showers at a National Guard headquarters.

    Even during a disaster, most people want to

    Possible Answer: do normal things like stay clean.
    _____

3. The Red Cross spent $44 million during the floods of 1993.

    Money is always necessary to

    Possible Answer: help bring relief and make repairs
    _____

Grammar: More Plural Spellings

- Some **nouns** have irregular **plural forms**.

Write the plural form of each noun in parentheses ().

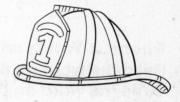

1. Hundreds of (person) helped after the flood. _____people_____

2. Many (life) were in danger. _____lives_____

3. The (fireman) and police helped. _____firemen_____

Write a sentence using one of the plural nouns from above.

4. Answers will vary.
    _____

Name _____

Vocabulary: Context Clues/Within a Paragraph
Read the paragraph. See the underlined words. Write the context clues that help to describe the underlined words.

We were all <u>devastated</u>. People everywhere were overwhelmed with grief because of the hurricane. After the hurricane, people from all over the country came to help. It could have been a <u>calamity</u>, but a great disaster was avoided because of all the people who came to <u>mitigate</u> the problem. They made the situation less stressful and less painful by helping those in need. People volunteered to <u>administer</u> medication. They gave medicine to help the sick, and the people were thankful for the help of the volunteers. They are true heroes.

1. devastated ___overwhelmed with grief___

2. calamity ___great disaster___

3. mitigate ___made the situation less stressful and less painful___

4. administer ___gave medicine to help___

Write one sentence. Use one of the underlined words from above.

5. ___Answers will vary.___

Phonics: Words with /ô/, /ou/, /oi/, /oo/
Read the word on the left. See the underlined letters. Write the word on the line that has the same vowel sound as the underlined letters.

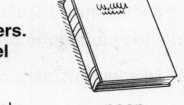

1. h<u>oo</u>k	book	core	book	noon
2. m<u>ou</u>nd	ground	floor	ground	sod
3. f<u>oy</u>er	employ	aid	employ	nurse
4. c<u>au</u>ght	daughter	new	drown	daughter
5. gl<u>oo</u>m	soon	soon	more	plum

Name _____

Comprehension: Make Generalizations

Read the paragraph below. Then write a checkmark on the line next to each sentence that is a good generalization. Use information in the paragraph and facts you already know, to help you decide which generalizations are good ones.

Every so often, a pod, or group, of whales mistakenly arrives on land. The whales are beached or stuck on land. This places the whales in extreme danger. They need the help of humans. On land, whales may become overheated. Whales do not sweat to cool down like humans. Helpers can gently splash water on the whales to help keep them cool. It is important not to splash water into a whale's blowhole which is used for breathing. This may cause the whale to drown. The whales are afraid and are not used to human noise. Helpers are also advised to have a happy mood because the whales can sense their moods. Only small whales can be carried by a group of people back into the water. Large whales cannot be turned or pushed because their body weight will break their ribs. Offering a helping hand to frightened whales is a great way to show concern for an ancient ocean creature.

1. ____√____ People who are helping a beached whale should never splash water into the whale's blowhole.

2. _____ Small whales are friendlier than large whales.

3. ____√____ Beached whales always need to be kept cool.

4. ____√____ Most whales are sensitive to the moods of those around them.

5. _____ Whales are found on beaches only during the summer.

Grammar: More Plural Spellings

Read the words below. Use the plural form of the word in a sentence.

1. calf ___Possible Answer: Many calves were stranded on farms during the flood.___

2. hoof ___Answers will vary, but must use hooves.___

3. person ___Answers will vary, but must use people.___

© Macmillan/McGraw-Hill

Name _____

Vocabulary: Dictionary/Idioms

- An **idiom** is a group of words that has a different meaning from the meaning of each word on its own. For example, *come in handy* means "useful."

Circle the correct meaning of the idioms underlined in each sentence.

1. No one in the kingdom would <u>take lightly</u> the disappearance of the princess.

   a. think it was unimportant   **c.** feel it was a mistake

   b. believe   **d.** think it didn't happen

2. The three ladies thought <u>around the clock</u> about the princess and her disappearance.

   a. when it got late   **c.** all the time

   b. during the night   **d.** when they woke up

3. Eventually, the princess reappeared at the castle <u>safe and sound</u>.

   a. unharmed   **c.** looking her best

   b. tired   **d.** feeling sad

Phonics: VCCV and VCCCV Patterns

Rewrite the words you see on the lines below, dividing each word into two syllables. Write a dash (-) between the two syllables in each word.

wallet	necklace	kingdom	pumpkin
factor	pantry	mental	barren
wal-let	neck-lace	king-dom	pump-kin
fac-tor	pan-try	men-tal	bar-ren

Comprehension: Identify Problem and Solution
- A story has a **problem** that characters need to fix.
- The **solution** is the way to fix the problem.

Answer the following questions about problems and solutions in _The Sad Prince_.

1. How did Beryl solve the problem of feeling sad because of being underground? He would become human and travel through the mountain and spend time with the animals that lived there.

2. Why is it a problem for Beryl to be in love with Princess Amber? A princess would not love a gnome.

3. How did Beryl bring Princess Amber into his gnome world? Beryl created a beautiful pool of water and Princess Amber stepped into the pool. Then, Beryl brought her underground.

4. Even though Beryl's underground kingdom was beautiful, what problem did Princess Amber have? She had a strong feeling of sadness.

Grammar: Possessive Nouns
- **Possessive nouns** show ownership of something.

Write the possessive form of each noun in parentheses ().

1. Prince Beryl had a (gnome) special powers. gnome's

2. The (gnomes) mine was very rich, and they prospered. gnomes'

3. The (princess) friends talked about the ball. princess's

4. The (prince) palace was sumptuous. prince's

Name _____

Vocabulary: Dictionary/Idioms
Read the sentences below. Choose an idiom from the box that means the same thing as the underlined words.

a piece of cake	sweeten the pot
cut to the chase	see eye to eye

1. The household chores were <u>easily done</u>. _____ a piece of cake _____

2. I'm glad we <u>agree completely</u> on who should be the prince's wife.
   see eye to eye _____

3. To <u>make the situation more appealing</u>, I will give you a prize if you help me fight the dragon. _____ sweeten the pot _____

4. I want you to <u>get to the point</u> and tell me what happened to the princess.
   cut to the chase _____

Phonics: VCCV and VCCCV Patterns
Write each word under the letter pattern that matches it. The first pattern, VCCV, shows two consonants in a row as in *picnic*. The second pattern, VCCC, shows three consonants in a row as in *sumptuous*.

factor	pantry	ballot	pumpkin

VCCV   **VCCCV**

factor   pumpkin
_____   _____

ballot   pantry
_____   _____

Comprehension: Identify Problem and Solution
Read the folktale. Then write about the problems and solutions.

Jack and his mother did not have any money to buy food. On market day, Jack's mother told him to sell their one cow for a good price. No one wanted to buy the cow. One man said he would buy the cow in exchange for a few beans. He told Jack that the beans were magic. When Jack showed his mother the beans, she was very angry. She threw the beans out the window. The next morning, Jack saw a giant beanstalk, reaching to the sky. Jack climbed it and found a castle filled with riches. Each day, Jack climbed the beanstalk and brought home more riches from the castle. Soon though, the angry giant who lived in the castle caught Jack. Jack escaped and raced down the beanstalk. Quickly he chopped down the beanstalk so that the giant could not follow him. Jack and his mother had enough riches to live on and did not miss their cow or the beanstalk.

Possible answers:

List two problems in this folktale:

a. Jack and his mother did not have money.

b. Nobody wanted to buy the cow.

List the solutions.

a. Jack went to sell their cow.

b. Jack sold the cow for beans.

Grammar: Possessive Nouns
Change each phrase below into its possessive form.

1. the crown of the princess the princess's crown

2. the muffler of the maids the maids' muffler

3. the magic of the prince the prince's magic

4. the palace of the king the king's palace

Name _____

Vocabulary: Thesaurus/Dictionary/Synonyms
• **Synonyms** are words that have a similar meaning. You can find synonyms in a thesaurus.

Find these words in a thesaurus. Then write the synonyms for the underlined words in each sentence. Answers will vary, but may include:

outskirts	rendezvous	disease	frigid

1. The <u>outskirts</u> of Anchorage are very beautiful. _____ edges _____

2. People in Anchorage have <u>rendezvous</u> for sled dog races. _____ meetings _____

3. About eighty years ago, the Great Serum Race saved children who were dying from a <u>disease</u> called diphtheria. _____ illness _____

4. Alaskan huskies are dogs with thick coats so they do well in <u>frigid</u> weather. _____ freezing _____

Write a sentence using one of the words from above.

5. Answers will vary. _____

Phonics: V/CV and VC/V Patterns
Write each word, and put a dash (-) between the two syllables.

1. secure _____ se-cure _____   4. resist _____ re-sist _____

2. vanish _____ van-ish _____   5. fever _____ fe-ver _____

3. unit _____ u-nit _____   6. panic _____ pan-ic _____

Comprehension: Identify Sequence of Events

- A **sequence** is the order of events in a story.

Number the events listed in the correct sequence, using what you know from *Sled Dogs*.

3 _____ An epidemic of diphtheria required sled dogs to deliver medicine to Nome, Alaska in 1925.

1 _____ During the gold rush in the late 1800s, teams of sled dogs traveled into town to get supplies for miners.

4 _____ Dorothy Page organized a centennial race along the Iditarod.

2 _____ During winter, miners couldn't work and started to have meetings, or rendezvous, and race sled dogs.

5 _____ Joe Redington wanted to make the Iditarod an annual event.

Grammar: Appositives

- An **appositive** is a word or group of words that identifies or tells more about the noun that it follows.
- **Commas** are used to set off most appositives from the rest of the sentence.

Write the appositive in each sentence and the noun it describes.

1. Hundreds of people take part in the Iditarod, a race in Alaska.

   a race in Alaska; Iditarod
   _____

2. Some sled dogs live in Anchorage's outskirts, or outer edge.

   outer edge; outskirts
   _____

Write a sentence of your own using an appositive.

3. Answers will vary.
   _____

Name _____

Vocabulary: Thesaurus/Dictionary/Synonyms
Read the thesaurus entries below. Then answer the questions about synonyms.

> **plenty,** *n.* — *Syn.* abundant, ample, excess, lots
> **plod,** *v.* — *Syn.* continue, lumber, persist, trudge, walk

1. What are the synonyms for *plenty*?

   abundant, ample, excess, lots _____

2. Rewrite the following sentence, replacing the word *plod* with one of its synonyms.

   They plod along the path to their home.

   Possible answer: They continue along the path to

   their home.

3. How do you find synonyms for a word in a thesaurus?

   Possible answer: Find the word, which is listed

   in alphabetical order in the thesaurus. Then

   look at the words after the entry word to find the

   synonyms.

Phonics: V/CV and VC/V Patterns
Read the words below. Write the syllables for each word on the lines.

1. secure _____ se _____ + _____ cure _____

2. hero _____ he _____ + _____ ro _____

3. inactive _____ in _____ + _____ ac _____ + _____ tive _____

Comprehension: Identify Sequence of Events
Read the paragraph below. Write the missing events in the sequence.

The roads were not cleared from the last snowfall, but Margaret needed a doctor quickly. Tomas needed to get Dr. Billings. Tomas built up the fire for Margaret. He harnessed the dogs and left. When Tomas saw the stand of pine trees, he guided the dogs west. He hoped Dr. Billings would be home. Soon Tomas saw the small cottage ahead. Smoke rose out of the chimney, and he knew the doctor was at home. Tomas called out, "Dr. Billings! It's me, Tomas Velez. My wife, Margaret, is ill." The door opened and Dr. Billings waved. Back at home Margaret shivered with the chills. Dr. Billings rushed to her side.

1. Tomas built up the fire.

2. _He harnessed the dogs._

3. _Tomas saw the pine trees and guided the dogs west._

4. Tomas saw smoke rising from Dr. Billings's chimney.

5. _Tomas called out to Dr. Billings._

6. Dr. Billings opened his door and waved.

7. _They rode back to Margaret._

Grammar: Appositives
Combine each sentence by forming appositives.

1. Balto saved many people during an epidemic. An epidemic is when many people are sick. _Balto saved many people during an epidemic, when many people were sick._

2. After Balto died, people built a memorial. A memorial is a place where people remember someone special. _After Balto died, people built a memorial, a place where people remember someone special._

Vocabulary An idiom is a group of words that has a different meaning from the meaning of each word on its own.

sweeten the pot—make the situation more appealing

pull someone's leg—play a joke on someone

come in handy—be useful

take it easy—don't hurry; relax

Phonics A word with two syllables can be divided between a **vowel (V)** and a **consonant (C) V/CV**, between a consonant and a vowel **VC/V**, or between two consonants **VC/C**. See the way the words are divided into syllables below.

V/CV	VC/V	VC/CV
se/cure a/dopt	cab/in nov/el	bas/ket hap/py

Comprehension A **sequence** is the order in which things happen. An **inference**, is a conclusion based on information you read and your previous knowledge.

Sequence of Events: Sarah baked a cake for Gina. Gina blew out the candles on the cake. Then everyone ate a slice of the cake. Afterwards, Gina opened her presents.

Inference: It was Gina's birthday.

Grammar An **appositive** is a word or group of words that identifies or tells more about the noun that it follows. Commas are used to set off most appositives from the rest of the sentence.

See the appositives below in bold print:

The sales clerk, **a grouchy person**, did not like to work overtime.

Shanti, **an excellent student**, was happy with her final grade.

The marathon race began in front of Wilson's Diner, **a popular restaurant**.

© Macmillan/McGraw-Hill

Circle the words that have a VC/V (cab/in) or VC/CV (con/vince) pattern.

1. a. (enthralled) b. plight c. (pennant)

2. a. phase b. (ravaged) c. (sweeten)

Choose the appositive for the underlined words.

3. Many tourists want to see the Mona Lisa, Leonardo DaVinci's most famous painting, at the Louvre Museum in Paris.

   a. the Louvre Museum in Paris

   (b.) Leonardo DaVinci's most famous painting

4. The mansion on the water, a quite luxurious place, is filled with antiques.

   (a.) a quite luxurious place

   b. is filled with antiques

Circle errors in capitalization, abbreviations, and underlining titles. Fill in your answers on the lines.

5. _____in._____ Michael Clemens was less than 5 ft., 7 (inc.) tall. He was the shortest football player

6. _____NFL_____ ever drafted to the (Nfl.) When everyone told him he was too small, he worked hard to

7. _____Pinball_____ be faster and smarter on the field. They gave him the nickname (pinball.)

8. _running back_ Clemens then moved to Canada and played for the CFL. As a (Running Back,) Clemens broke many football records.

9. _____Toronto_____ After retiring from football, he became the head coach for the (toronto) Argonauts.

10. List the sequence of events in Michael Clemens's life.

He was drafted to the NFL, he moved to Canada, he played for the Toronto Argonauts, he retired from football, he became a head coach, he wrote a book.

Name _____

Phonics: Plurals, VC/CV Patterns

**Read the story. Circle the plural words in the first paragraph.
Circle the words in the second paragraph with a VC/CV pattern.
Then answer the questions.**

It was a gloomy day in the pouring rain. The (media) were
broadcasting the game to (radios) all over the state. The pitcher
stood on the mound, preparing for his final throw. Another strike
would decide the outcome of the game. The pitcher was nervous
but he calmed down when he thought about his (heroes), Bob Feller
and Roberto Clemente. Their (lives) were an inspiration to him.

He tried to stretch his (shoulder). It hurt. Later, he would
have to see the (doctor). But at this moment, his team relied
on him. The team's goal was to win the (pennant). It was all they
desired. The catcher gave a (signal). The pitcher threw the ball.

Comprehension: Make Inferences

1. What traits does the pitcher have? How do you know?

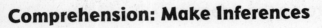

   courage, determination; he plays when he's in

   pain; he wants to reach his goal.

2. Draw and complete an Inferences Diagram for this story with text clues
   and prior knowledge to support inferences.

Text Clues and Prior Knowledge	Inference

Text clue—Another strike
would determine the
outcome. Inference—This
was an important game.
Text Clue—His shoulder
hurt, but he kept playing.
Inference—He had strength
and courage.

Name _____

Vocabulary
Read each sentence. Circle the letter of the word that best completes the sentence.

1. The sales clerk was ____ because a customer was rude to her.
   - **a.** furious
   - **(b.)** grouchy
   - **c.** interested
   - **d.** sweet

2. The quesadillas were delicious but the jalapeño peppers made them really ____.
   - **a.** tasteless
   - **b.** soft
   - **(c.)** spicy
   - **d.** crisp

3. After Raymond fell and twisted his ankle, he got up and ____ off the field.
   - **(a.)** hobbled
   - **b.** raced
   - **c.** swam
   - **d.** hopped

4. Cars belong on streets and ____ walk on sidewalks.
   - **a.** motorcycles
   - **b.** birds
   - **c.** elephants
   - **(d.)** pedestrians

Write the meaning of each idiom.

5. sweeten the pot _to make the situation more appealing_

6. pull someone's leg _to play a joke on someone_

Phonics: V/CV, VC/V, and VC/CV Patterns
Circle the word that has V/CV, VC/V, or VC/CV pattern in each group.

7. sweet   (human)   phase

8. starve   type   (basket)

Grammar: Appositives, Common and Proper Nouns, Possessive Nouns

Choose the answer that describes the underlined words.

1. There are many <u>pedestrians</u>, or people walking, on the street.
   a. on the street   **b.** people walking

2. Hundreds of people take part in the <u>Iditarod</u>, a race in Alaska.
   a. people take part   **b.** a race in Alaska

Choose the set of nouns to complete each sentence.

3. The nickname for our school's team is the ____ and they won the division ____.
   a. wildcats, Trophy
   b. Wildcats, trophy

4. The food served by ____ was very spicy, and the ____ was beautiful.
   a. Mrs. Ramos, Spanish music
   b. mrs. Ramos, spanish music

Choose the possessive form of each noun in parentheses.

5. The (gnomes) mine was very rich, but the (prince) palace was sumptuous.
   a. gnome's, prince's
   b. gnomes', princes'
   c. gnomes', prince's

6. The (princess) friends lived on the outskirts of the city in their (parents) homes.
   a. princess's, parent's
   b. princess's, parents'
   c. princes's, parents's

Editing: Underlining, Capitalizing, Abbreviations, Plural Forms

Read the story. Look for errors in underlining, capitalizing, abbreviations, and using correct plural forms. Circle the errors and write the corrections on the lines.

Natalya's Dream

When Natalya read the book, First on the Moon, by mr. Neil Armstrong, it inspired her to become an Astronaut. Natalya knew that only a few people become astronauts. All childs dream of going to the moon, she thought. How would she succeed? Natalya studied harder than everyone else in all of her class's. She went to Space Camp, and then she attended Space Academy. When she went to college, Natalya took classes in astronomy and physics. Most important of all, she had determination. Natalya made her dream come true. She became an astronaut with NASA on Jan 12.

First on the Moon
1. _____

Mr.
2. _____

astronaut
3. _____

children
4. _____

classes
5. _____

Jan.
6. _____

Comprehension: Make Inferences, Sequence

1. Write a statement that is an inference about the story.

   Possible answer: A dream combined with hard work can make that dream come true.

2. What steps did Natalya take to become an astronaut?

   She studied harder than everyone else, she went to Space Camp, and then she attended Space Academy. In college, she took classes in astronomy and physics.

Name _____

Vocabulary: Word Parts/Base Words

• Adding a **word part** (a prefix or suffix) to a base word creates new words that are related.

Add each suffix to the base word *employ*. Write what each new word means using a dictionary for support.

| employ | -ee | -er | -ment | -able |

Word

Meaning Possible Answers:

1. _employee_ ___person who works for someone___
   ___else or for a company___

2. _employer_ ___boss or company for whom a___
   ___person works___

3. _employment_ ___having work___

4. _employable_ ___able to work___

Write a sentence using one of the words you defined.

Answers will vary.

5. _____

Phonics: Accented Syllables

Underline words in which the initial syllable is accented or stressed.
Circle words in which the final syllable is accented or stressed.

1. (en-roll)

2. should-er (underlined)

3. (ac-cept)

4. wealth-y (underlined)

5. (re-pair)

6. sea-son (underlined)

Name _____

Comprehension: Analyze Character, Setting, and Plot

- The **setting** is the time and place of a story.
- **Characters** are the people who take part in the events of the story's **plot**.

Read the details from *The Summer of Surprises*. Write *character*, *setting*, or *plot* on the lines.

1. ___character___ Benny lived one week with his father and one week with his mother.

2. ___setting___ It was a 200-year-old house built of adobe bricks.

3. ___plot___ Benny's mother can't finish writing, so they both travel to the Southwest for ideas.

Write one more detail about the story's main character, setting, or plot.

4. ___Possible answer: The main character, Benny, does not want to go to New Mexico.___

Grammar: Action Verbs; Direct and Indirect Objects

- An **action verb** tells what the subject of a sentence does or did.
- A **direct object** is a noun or pronoun that receives the action of the verb.
- An **indirect object** answers *to what*, *for what*, *to whom*, or *for whom*.

Circle each action verb. Underline the indirect object once and the direct object twice.

1. Isabel wrote the Earth a letter.

2. The dog gave Cole his paw.

3. The dog fetched Kip the ball.

4. Benny showed his mom the vase.

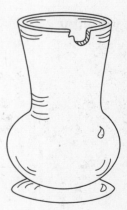

Name _____

Vocabulary: Word Parts/Base Words
Read the words below. Write the base word on the line.

1. employee _____ employ _____

2. gloated _____ gloat _____

3. vigorously _____ vigorous _____

4. wealthy _____ wealth _____

5. installment _____ install _____

Write a sentence using one of the base words from above.

6. _____ Answers will vary. _____

Phonics: Accented Syllables
Read the words below aloud. Write the syllables of each word.
Circle the accented syllable.

Accented Syllable

1. secure	se	+	(cure)
2. debate	de	+	(bate)
3. county	(coun)	+	ty
4. escape	es	+	(cape)
5. wealthy	(weal)	+	thy

© Macmillan/McGraw-Hill

Comprehension: Analyze Character, Setting, and Plot
Read the story below. Then, answer questions about the story's characters, setting, and plot.

Last August, my family and I took an amazing trip. My dad is a geologist, and my mom is an artist. They told me about the rock formations in New Mexico and the artists who live there. I wasn't excited at first, but my dad said if we went to the Carlsbad Caverns, we might see almost 300,000 bats. We drove the whole way in our mini-van. As soon as we passed our first red rock formation, I couldn't stop looking out the window. We spent one day in the town looking at art. Then, we drove to the caverns. We were told to sit quietly near the entrance to one of the main caves. As my dad predicted, thousands of bats flew out. It was an amazing sight!

1. Describe one setting in the story. Possible Answer:
   Part of the story takes place in a mini-van.

2. Write two details about the main character's mom and dad.

   a. The main character's mom is an artist.

   b. The main character's dad is a geologist.

3. How did the main character's feelings about the trip to New Mexico change from the beginning of the story to the end?
   At the beginning, he did not want to go, and at the end, he was glad that they had gone.

Grammar: Action Verbs; Direct and Indirect Objects
Read the sentences below. Circle the action verb. Write DO if the underlined word is a direct object. Write IO if the underlined word is an indirect object.

1. Miguel (found) a small <u>town</u> in the Southwest to visit. _____ DO _____

2. The people of the town (made) <u>visitors</u> turquoise jewelry. _____ IO _____

3. The heat (melted) the <u>ice</u> in the drink. _____ DO _____

Name _____

Vocabulary: Dictionary/Word Origins

- You can find information about the history of a word in the **dictionary**.

Look up the meaning of the following words and write from what language each word comes.

1. limousine   _____French_____

2. promenade   _Latin, Old French_

3. replica   _Latin, Italian_

4. mystery   _Greek, Latin_

5. paragraph   _Greek, Latin_

Write English words you know that come from other languages.

6. _Answers will vary._ _____ _____

Phonics: Words with Final /ər/

- The words *stroller* and *platter* end in /ər/.

stroller

platter

Say the words *matter* and *flavor*. These are examples of words that end in /ər/. In each group, choose the word that ends in /ər/.

1. accord   tarp   gutter   _gutter_

2. guitar   waiter   call   _waiter_

3. far   behavior store   _behavior_

4. ruble   more   author   _author_

Name _____

Comprehension: Draw Conclusions

• A **conclusion** is an idea that is based on supporting facts.

Read the conclusions. Match the conclusion with the story detail from *The Hometown Homework* that supports it.

Story Details

1. ____A____ Mr. Mora's writing assignment requires students to write about what they know.

2. ____D____ Julie says she loves to write, but needs help with revisions.

3. ____B____ Julie is upset by Mr. Mora's writing assignment and thinks what she has won't excite the judges.

4. ____C____ Peter writes to Julie that she "wrote to the right person."

Conclusions

A. Mr. Mora wants his students to become better observers of their own world, rather than a made-up world.

B. Julie thinks writing judges prefer stories filled with sensational, out-of-this-world details.

C. Peter thinks he and Julie will get along well.

D. Julie has great ideas for writing, but sometimes she doesn't know how to make improvements.

Grammar: Past and Future Tense: Verbs

• The **tense** of a verb tells the time when an action takes place.

Circle the verb in each sentence, then write the tense.

1. Julie (wrote) a letter to Peter._____past_____

2. Mr. Mora (gave) her the assignment._____past_____

3. Peter (will read) her letter._____future_____

Vocabulary: Dictionary/Word Origins
Read the word origins and definitions below. Then answer the questions.

Word Origins

ancestor	[Latin *antecessor*] predecessor; person from whom one is descended
embark	[Middle French *embarquer*] begin an undertaking; set out; start
limousine	[French *Limousin*] former French province; a large passenger vehicle
wander	[Old English *wandrian*] move here and there without any special purpose

1. What is the origin of the word *limousine*? __French__

2. What is the origin of the word *ancestor*? __Latin__

3. What is the origin of the word *wander*? __Old English__

4. What is the origin of the word *embark*? __Middle French__

Phonics: Words with Final /ər/
Choose the word that ends in /ər/ as in the words *actor*, *gutter*, and *similar*. Circle the letters that make /ər/, and then write the word.

1. messeng(er)   hear   there   ___messenger___

2. door   mirr(or)   core   ___mirror___

3. care   car   singul(ar)   ___singular___

4. clam(or)   claim   hear   ___clamor___

Comprehension: Draw Conclusions
Read the letter below. Write a detail from the letter that supports each conclusion.

Dear Friendly Neighbor Award Committee,

I would like to nominate Mrs. Finker for this year's Friendly Neighbor Award. She waves to anyone who passes by and not everyone does this. Mrs. Finker is older than the other neighbors, but her yard is still neat. Many times she cuts her flowers from her garden and delivers bouquets to neighbors. She never minds when our soccer ball flies into her yard. I'd like Mrs. Finker to win because she is a wonderful example of a friendly neighbor.

Sincerely,

Tomas "Tommie" de Molina

1. **Detail:** Mrs. Finker's yard is kept neat and she has a garden.
   Conclusion: Mrs. Finker spends time in her yard.

2. **Detail:** Mrs. Finker cuts her flowers and delivers bouquets.
   Conclusion: Mrs. Finker is proud of her flower garden.

3. What does the letter tell you about Tommie? Draw a conclusion about the kind of person Tommie is. Possible Answer: He notices things and is respectful to older people.

Grammar: Past and Future Tenses: Verbs
Read the words below. Write the missing verbs under the correct tense.

	Past	Present	Future
1.	wrote	write	will write
2.	embarked	embark	will embark
3.	lamented	lament	will lament

Name _____

Vocabulary: Context Clues/Within a Sentence
- **Context clues** hint at, or describe unfamiliar words.

Circle context clues that hint at the meaning of each underlined word.

1. Deposits of fossil fuels can't be <u>replenished</u>, or made full again.

2. There are different ways to <u>generate</u>, or produce, electricity.

3. Hydroelectric plants convert the power of falling water into electricity. This is not an <u>adverse</u> or negative way to generate electricity.

4. Water is a <u>renewable</u> resource because it can be replaced.

Write a sentence using one underlined word from above.

5. _Answers will vary._ _____

Phonics: Words with Final /ən/ and /əl/
- The word *organ* ends in /ən/. The word *whistle* ends in /əl/.

organ

whistle

Write the word that ends in /ən/.

| 1. | carton | camping | acorn | carton |
| 2. | raisin | tour | ton | raisin |

Write the word that ends in /əl/.

| 3. | cable | mall | recall | cable |
| 4. | vertical | steel | until | vertical |

Comprehension: Identify Cause and Effect
- A **cause** is the reason for an action or event.
- An **effect** is the result of an action or event.

Complete each pair of causes and effects using facts from
Energy and Our World.

Cause	Effect
1. Power plants burn coal and oil.	Electricity is produced.
2. Oil tankers leak oil.	Animals are poisoned.
3. An engine releases nitrogen oxides.	Smog is created.

Grammar: Main and Helping Verbs/Tenses
- A **verb phrase** consists of a helping verb and a main verb.

On the first line write a helping verb for the sentence. Then write whether the verb phrase is in the present, past, or future tense.

1. Our nonrenewable resources _____ disappear right now.

   _____can_____   _____Present_____

2. We _____ generate energy in many ways in the future.

   _____will_____   _____Future_____

3. We _____ using different sources of energy in the past.

   _____were_____   _____Past_____

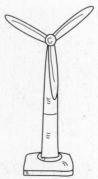

Name _____

Vocabulary: Context Clues/Within a Sentence

Read the sentences below. Circle the word or phrase that is the context clue for each underlined word.

1. The <u>adverse</u> conditions were (harmful) to her health.

2. The <u>apparatus</u> was a (machine) that could run on solar power.

3. Coal <u>generates</u>, or (produces,) heat when burned.

4. Wind is a <u>renewable</u> source of energy, so it (cannot be used up).

Write a sentence using one of the underlined words from above. Include a new context clue that describes the underlined word. Circle the context clue.

5. *Answers will vary.*
  _____

Phonics: Words with Final /ən/ and /əl/

Read the words below aloud. Write the word that has the same sound as the underlined letters.

1. gall<u>on</u> ____*carton*____ carton   tone   groan

2. foss<u>il</u> ____*label*____ fast   sight   label

3. renewab<u>le</u> ____*fumble*____ knew   rent   fumble

4. burd<u>en</u> ____*curtain*____ curtain   rain   stain

Comprehension: Identify Cause and Effect
Read the paragraph below. Then, write causes and effects using the information in the paragraph.

When the weather is warm, the backyards in my neighborhood look different. Everyone hangs laundry out to dry. This takes more of my energy because I have to help my mom hang the laundry, but we use less electric energy. Drying laundry outside takes longer than in a dryer, but our laundry has a nice fresh-air smell. One day, there was a sudden rain shower. It was as if our laundry was washed twice.

1. **Write the causes for each effect below.**

   Effect: Backyards look different.

   Cause: Everyone hangs laundry out to dry.

   Effect: I use more of my energy.

   Cause: I help my mom hang the laundry.

2. **Write the effects for each cause below.**

   Cause: Laundry hangs on the clothesline for a few hours.

   Effect: The laundry has a fresh-air smell.

   Cause: There was a sudden rain shower.

   Effect: The laundry was washed twice.

Grammar: Main and Helping Verbs/Tenses
Circle the correct helping verb in the parentheses. Write the verb tense on the line.

1. Windmills (can, have) make renewable energy. present

2. We (being, will) conserve energy in our household. future

3. Sara (was, have) thinking about recycling. past

Vocabulary: Word Parts/Prefixes

- A **prefix** is a word part that is added to the beginning of a word. Prefixes change the meaning of words.

Choose the word that best completes the sentences based on the meaning of the following prefixes.

pro- = extend, be in favor	**pre-** = before
re- = again, back	**dis-** = opposite, reverse

1. The time before people kept written records of history is called ____pre____history.

2. The prehistoric paintings of Lascaux are so fragile that they can ____dis____integrate easily.

3. The paintings have been protected in order to ____pro____long their existence.

4. The French government is not going to ____re____open these areas.

Write a sentence in which you use a word with a prefix.

5. ____Answers will vary._____

Phonics: Words with Prefixes
Say the following words and underline the prefix in each one.

1. preschool

2. incomplete

3. unknown

4. discolored

5. superhero

6. reposition

Name _____

Comprehension: Summarize

• To **summarize** is to tell the most important facts about a topic in a few sentences.

1. **Place a checkmark next to the sentences that could be included in a summary about *Cave Paintings*.**

   a. ____√____ Four young friends discovered the cave paintings at Lascaux in 1940.

   b. _____ Limestone easily dissolves in water.

   c. ____√____ The Lascaux cave has seven different areas with paintings.

   d. ____√____ Scientists agree that the ancient artists painted by the light of fat-burning lamps.

   e. ____√____ The paintings in the Lascaux cave were painted during the last Ice Age.

   f. _____ The Magdalenians used utensils, or tools, made from flint, or stone.

2. **Explain the reason you did not choose one of the sentences as a summary sentence.**

   Possible answer: Sentence f tells information that is too specific to be included in a summary.

Grammar: Linking Verbs, Predicate Nouns and Adjectives

• A **linking verb** links a sentence's subject to a sentence's predicate noun or predicate adjective.

Circle each linking verb. Underline each predicate noun or predicate adjective.

1. The Magdalenians (were) civilized people.

2. They (were) artists.

3. The animals (look) real.

Name _____

Vocabulary: Word Parts/Prefixes
Read the prefixes and their meanings below. Then write the definition of the words below.

Prefixes

pre- = before	**un-** = not	**extra-** = beyond

1. prehistory _before recorded history_____

2. extraordinary _beyond what is ordinary_____

3. preview _to view or display beforehand_____

4. unknown _not known_____

Phonics: Words with Prefixes
Read the word below. Write the prefix, the base word, and the meaning on the lines below.

	Prefix	Base Word	Meaning
1. uncover	un	cover	to remove cover
2. enrich	en	rich	to make richer
3. disappear	dis	appear	to become invisible
4. indistinct	in	distinct	not distinct
5. inhuman	in	human	not human

Comprehension: Summarize
Read the paragraph below. Then answer the questions that follow.

According to archaeologists, many cave paintings include only images of animals, humans, or symbols. The Lascaux cave paintings show 600 images of animals. The majority of the pictures show horses. A few pictures are of bison. There is only one example of a human. Symbols include dots and lines. Some rectangular figures were painted, too. The cave paintings give archaeologists clues about the lives of prehistoric people. It is important that the cave paintings are protected because otherwise, this clue to the past will be lost. The paint used in the Lascaux cave is easily damaged by people's breath; therefore, the cave is no longer open for tours.

1. What images are included in most cave paintings around the world?
   Most include animals, humans, or symbols.

2. What types of images do the Lascaux cave paintings mainly show?
   The Lascaux cave paintings show mainly horses.

3. Why is the Lascaux cave closed for tours?
   Human breath damages the cave paintings.

4. Why do archaeologists study cave paintings?
   Archeologists want to find clues to the past.

Grammar: Linking Verbs, Predicate Nouns and Adjectives
Complete each sentence with a linking verb. Underline the predicate noun or predicate adjective.

1. The trenches _____ were _____ deep.

2. The archaeologist _____ appears _____ anxious about the dig.

3. The discoveries _____ are _____ artifacts from prehistoric times.

4. The ancient utensil _____ looks _____ fragile.

Name _____

Vocabulary: Analogy/Synonyms

• **Synonyms** are words that have the same or nearly the same meaning.

Choose words from the word bank to complete the following analogies.

| anonymous | annoyance | significance | supporting |

1. role is to part as importance is to ___significance___

2. practicing is to rehearsing as supporting is to ___sponsoring___

3. dazzling is to brilliant as unknown is to ___anonymous___

4. impersonation is to imitation as nuisance is to ___annoyance___

Write a sentence using a word from the box.

5. ___Answers will vary.___

Phonics: Adding *-ion*, *-ation*

• The endings *-ion* and *-ation* are used to form nouns from verbs.

Match the verbs with their nouns and say each pair of words.

1. __d__ connect   a. representation

2. __e__ illustrate   b. observation

3. __c__ instruct   c. instruction

4. __a__ represent   d. connection

5. __f__ inspire   e. illustration

6. __b__ observe   f. inspiration

© Macmillan/McGraw-Hill

Comprehension: Draw Conclusions

- A **conclusion** is an idea based on supporting facts.
  You can draw a conclusion based on facts you read.

Match each detail from *The School Play* to the conclusion that it supports.

Details

a. Coach Linus asks the students to form a line and do fifty jumping jacks.

b. Joel thinks that as the lead actor he should be director, and Kasey thinks that without Mr. Wheeler, he should be director.

c. Joel wants to do karate; Erica wants to teach people to respect the homes of animals; Kasey has suggestions about scenery.

d. Erica stopped coming to rehearsals.

Conclusions

1. ____d____ Erica is despondent and does not like the changes that have been made to her script.

2. ____b____ Kasey and Joel both want to be in charge.

3. ____c____ The students have many different ideas, and the play is suffering because of it.

4. ____a____ Coach Linus wants to direct the play in the same way he coaches baseball.

Grammar: Irregular Verbs

- **Irregular verbs** do not end in -*d* or -*ed* to form the past tense.

Circle the past tense form of the verb.

1. The author (was, will be) anonymous.

2. Teddy (wears, wore) a bear costume.

3. Erica (wrote, writes) the play.

Vocabulary: Analogy/Synonyms
Match the word with its synonym.

1. significance ___b___   **a.** supporting

2. anonymous ___c___   **b.** importance

3. array ___d___   **c.** unknown

4. sponsoring ___a___   **d.** variety

Write a sentence using one of the words from above.

5. ___Answers will vary._____

Phonics: Adding *-ion* and *-ation*
Read the boldfaced word. Then read the word with the added suffixes *-ion* or *-ation*. Make a checkmark (√) if there is a spelling change in the base word.

1. **inspire**   inspiration ___√___

2. **act**   action _____

3. **instruct**   instruction _____

4. **observe**   observation ___√___

5. **represent**   representation _____

Comprehension: Draw Conclusions

Read the paragraph below. Then, place a checkmark (√) in front of the conclusions that are supported by details in the paragraph.

A Broadway show in New York City involves very talented performers. It takes a lot of determination to become part of a Broadway show. Thousands of people try out, or audition, for parts as singers, dancers, or actors. Only a small number of them will be given a role. People who want to perform on Broadway may spend years trying to be discovered by those who direct the shows. Many people begin training when they are children. Others decide they want to perform after they have attended school. On Broadway, dreams can come true after many long hours of rehearsals.

Conclusions:

a. ____√____ Some of the best actors, dancers, and singers perform in the Broadway shows in New York.

b. _____ Tickets to Broadway shows are expensive.

c. ____√____ It is difficult to earn a role in a Broadway show.

d. ____√____ Many Broadway performers have trained since they were children.

e. _____ Actors, dancers, and singers need to have part-time jobs doing other things.

Grammar: Irregular Verbs

Write the missing tenses of each irregular verb.

Present	Past
1. sing	sang
2. go	went
3. mimic	mimicked
4. think	thought

Name _____

Vocabulary **Context clues** are words that help explain unfamiliar words in a sentence. Look at the sentences below and see the context clues that help explain the meaning of the underlined words.

Sebastian <u>gleefully</u>, or *merrily*, packed for his journey to Africa.

Coretta is an <u>employee</u> of the hospital and *works there* at night.

Phonics Some words end with **/ər/, /ən/,** or **/əl/.** Listen for these sounds in the words in the chart below.

/ər/	/ən/	/əl/
meager	weapon	struggle
senator	frighten	channel

Comprehension A **conclusion** is a fact based on supporting facts. Your conclusion should be based on the details from your reading and what you already know.

Jamil had been waiting for the train for twenty minutes. His nose was running, and he was rubbing his hands together to stay warm. Suddenly, he heard a loud train whistle in the distance. He got excited and took out his train ticket.

Conclusion Jamil is leaving on a train trip on a cold day.

Grammar An **action verb** is a word that shows action. It tells what the subject does or did. A **linking verb** connects the subject to a noun or adjective.

Action Janessa **skated** across the ice.
Linking The cookies **are** delicious.

Name _____

Match each vocabulary word with its meaning. Then circle a vocabulary word with /əl/.

1. mimics ___b___   a. amazing

2. (sensational) ___a___   b. imitates

3. precede ___d___   c. begin

4. embark ___c___   d. go before

Decide whether each word in bold print is a predicate noun or a predicate adjective.

5. He is an **employee**.

   (a.) predicate noun   b. predicate adjective

6. Tina's car is **luxurious**.

   a. predicate noun   (b.) predicate adjective

Circle errors in punctuation and capitalization in the play below. Write the corrections near mistakes.

7. **Hajir:** Are you sure Father said we would find a treasure in the (attic.) We've been looking for hours!
   ?

8. **Noura:** Yes, that's what he said, but all I see are old clothes and books like this one.

9. *Noura holds up the book and a letter falls out from within the pages.*

10. **Noura:** Look, Hajir! It's a love letter from Grandpa to Grandma (yaseem!)
   Y

11. (Hajir) I guess father was right about finding treasure!

12. Who are the characters? What is the setting?

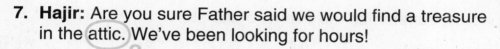
Characters—Hajir and Noura Setting—The attic

Name _____

Phonics: Words with Final /ər/, /ən/, /əl/

Read the story. Circle the words with final /ər/ in the first two sentences. Circle the words with final /ən/ and /əl/ in the rest of the text. Read the text a second time. Then answer the questions.

Sara is watching a (popular), scary movie. She likes it because it is (similar) to movies she has seen. It (frightens) her when a monster jumps out from behind a door, but she likes it. Sometimes, characters are walking at midnight in a dark (castle). Sara usually cheers for the monster when it (struggles) with another character.

Sara knows that the movie is almost over. She has a (suspicion) that her little brother is going to try to scare her. She hears him (stumble) over the carpet behind her, so she turns quickly. "Boo!" Sara yells, and her (little) brother jumps and (giggles).

Comprehension: Summarize

1. In your own words, summarize the events of the story.

   Sara is watching a scary movie. She thinks that her little brother will try to scare her, so she scares him instead.

2. Draw and complete a Summary Chart for this story.

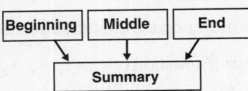

Beginning—Sara is watching a scary movie and thinking about why she likes it. Middle—Sara thinks her little brother wants to scare her. End—Sara scares him. Summary—Sara sees a scary movie and then scares her brother.

Name _____

Vocabulary

Read each sentence. Circle the letter of the word that best completes the sentence.

1. Francesca gave her daughter extra money to spend at an amusement park and the child ____ accepted it.

   a. politely   **b.** carelessly   **c.** gleefully   **d.** returned

2. The president came in a ____ with a driver and Secret Service agents.

   a. motorcycle   **b.** mansion

   c. limousine   **d.** go kart

   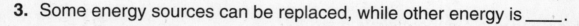

3. Some energy sources can be replaced, while other energy is ____.

   a. expensive   **b.** wasted   **c.** poisonous   **d.** nonrenewable

Use the underlined context clues in each sentence to help you find the answer.

4. Forks, knives, and spoons are different types of ____ or things to eat with.

   a. utensils   **b.** clothing   **c.** fabric   **d.** energy sources

5. My little brother Eric imitates, or ____, my actions all the time.

   a. invents   **b.** mimics   **c.** reduces   **d.** draws

6. Plants, trees, and flowers ____ and bloom in the spring and summer.

   a. flourish   **b.** germinate   **c.** generate   **d.** wither

Phonics: Words with Final /ər/ and /əl/
Circle the word with final /ər/ or /əl/ in each group.

7. sensational   provide   recall

8. embark   senator   precede

Name _____

Grammar: Linking Verbs, Predicate Nouns and Adjectives, Action Verbs, Direct and Indirect Objects

Find the linking verb in each sentence. Circle the letter of the answer.

1. The Magdalenians were civilized people who flourished long ago.

   a. were   **b.** civilized   **c.** flourished

2. There were many talented artists in the Old Southwest whose paintings looked real.

   a. talented, real   **b.** were, looked   **c.** many, paintings

Decide if the words in italics are predicate nouns or predicate adjectives. Circle the letter of the answer.

3. Juan became a *superstitious man*.

   a. predicate noun   **b.** predicate adjective

4. This resource is *renewable*.

   a. predicate noun   **b.** predicate adjective

Find the action verbs in the following sentence. Circle the letter of the answer.

5. The archaeologist slowly excavates the trenches with tools, and she works hard.

   a. slowly, hard   **b.** excavates, works

Find the direct objects in the following sentence. Circle the letter of the answer.

6. Emilia mimics me with her voice, then she tells Victor a story from the Old Southwest.

   a. Southwest, voice   **b.** me, story   **c.** Emilia, her

© Macmillan/McGraw-Hill

Name _____

Editing: Punctuating a Play, Capitalizing Proper Nouns

Read the play. Look for errors in punctuation and capitalization. Circle the errors and write the corrections on the lines.

A Great Idea

1. *Young Benjamin Franklin is flying his kite in an open field at night with his Brother James. Lightning is flashing everywhere, lighting up the sky.*

2. **Ben:** Look, James! Lightning is flashing! We can see mr. Bartholomew's entire field as clearly as if it were day!

   James: Yes, Ben, I see. However, I think you should be more careful. The lightning seems to be getting closer all the time!

3. **Ben.** Nonsense, James! We're quite safe where we are.

4. *Ben lets go of his Kite. It flies into the air. Lightning strikes the kite and burns it.*

5. **James.** Ben! Are you all right?

   Ben: Yes, I'm fine. James, think about the energy contained in that bolt of lightning! Could it be used to light homes in the same way that lightning

6. lights the Sky? There must be a way!

1. _____brother_____ 2. _____Mr._____ 3. _____Ben:_____

4. _____kite_____ 5. _____James:_____ 6. _____sky_____

Comprehension: Character, Setting, Plot, Draw Conclusions

1. Who are the characters? What is the plot? What is the setting?

   Characters—Ben and James Plot—Ben flies a kite during a rainstorm to experiment. Setting—an open field during a storm

2. Why do you think Ben is flying a kite during a rainstorm?

   He wants to experiment with energy from lightning.

Name _____

Vocabulary: Context Clues/Synonyms
- **Context clues** help explain the meaning of other words in a sentence.
- **Synonyms** are words with similar meanings.

Use context clues to figure out the meaning of the underlined word. Then circle one or more words that are synonyms of the underlined word.

1. People everywhere admire Marla Runyan, who is an <u>awesome</u> runner.

   (a.) amazing   **b.** ordinary   **c.** average   **(d.)** impressive

2. Marla couldn't see very well at the start of fourth grade because her eyesight was <u>deteriorating</u>.

   a. making progress   **c.** beginning

   (b.) getting worse   **d.** surfacing

3. Do you think Marla Runyan has reached the <u>summit</u> of her career?

   (a.) peak   **b.** challenge   **(c.)** top   **d.** end

Think of another synonym for awesome and rewrite sentence 1.

4. _Possible answer: People everywhere admire Marla Runyan, who is a fantastic runner._

Phonics: Words with -ion with Spelling Changes
The ending **-ion** changes a verb into a noun. Match the verbs with their nouns and say each pair of words.

1. ___d___ decide   **a.** division

2. ___c___ admit   **b.** explanation

3. ___b___ explain   **c.** admission

4. ___a___ divide   **d.** decision

Explain how the spelling of a verb above changes when you add -ion.

5. _Answers will vary._

Comprehension: Evaluate Author's Purpose
• An **author's purpose** is the author's reason for writing.

Circle the letter of the phrase that completes the sentence about the author's purpose.

1. Why did the author write about the difference between being blind and being legally blind? The author wrote
   a. to explain the meaning of the term legally blind.
   b. to persuade the reader to feel sympathy for blind people.
   c. to inform the reader about the number of people that are born blind.

2. Why did the author write that Marla's parents focused on the good news from the eye specialists? The author wrote
   a. to explain what happened after her doctor's appointment.
   b. to describe the positive attitude that Marla's parents had.
   c. to persuade readers to be positive about their health.

3. Why did the author write that Marla's vision didn't matter while she was on the running track? The author wrote
   a. to persuade readers to become runners.
   b. to explain macular degeneration in greater detail.
   c. to describe why Marla loved running.

Grammar: Pronouns and Antecedents
• An **antecedent** is the word or group of words to which a pronoun refers.

Write the pronoun and antecedent.

1. Marla qualified for the Olympics, even though she was legally blind.

   Pronoun: _____she_____   **Antecedent:** _____Marla_____

Write a sentence of your own with a pronoun and antecedent. Circle the pronoun. Draw an arrow from the pronoun to its antecedent.

2. Answers will vary.

Name _____

Vocabulary: Context Clues/Synonyms

Read the sentences below. Choose the synonym of each underlined word from the word bank.

> guidance   typical   peripheral   deteriorated

1. With the <u>direction</u> of her teacher, she was able to accomplish her goal. _____guidance_____

2. Although his hearing <u>worsened</u>, he still wrote and played his music. _____deteriorated_____

3. The eye doctor checked her <u>outer</u> vision. _____peripheral_____

4. The young boy was not a <u>usual</u> student because he didn't want to go out and play during recess with kids his age. _____typical_____

Phonics: Words with *-ion* with Spelling Changes

Match the base word with its *-ion* word.

1. explode   a. admission
2. explain   b. inclusion
3. include   c. explanation
4. admit   d. explosion
5. divide   e. division

Write a sentence using an *-ion* word from above.

6. _____Answers will vary._____

Comprehension: Evaluate Author's Purpose
Draw a line from each detail to the author's purpose for writing that detail.

Details

1. The first woman to swim the English Channel dies at 98.

2. People thought women couldn't swim the channel, so Gertrude Ederle proved that a woman could.

3. The city of New York held a parade in Gertrude's honor.

4. In her forties, Gertrude was entirely deaf due to a childhood sickness and years of being in the water.

Author's Purpose

a. The author wanted to inform readers about a person who made history.

b. The author wanted to describe people's enthusiasm after Gertrude accomplished her goal.

c. The author wanted to describe Gertrude Ederle's motivation for swimming.

d. The author wanted to explain the effects of Gertrude Ederle's health.

Grammar: Pronouns and Antecedents
Rewrite each sentence using the correct pronoun. Then underline the antecedent.

1. Champions know (he, they) have to work hard.
   Champions know they have to work hard.
   _____

2. Corrine says (she, you) admires long-distance runners.
   Corrine says she admires long-distance runners.
   _____

3. The challenges may be awesome, but (they, you) cannot stop you from succeeding.
   The challenges may be awesome, but they cannot stop you from succeeding.
   _____

Name _____

Vocabulary: Word Parts/Suffixes

- A **suffix** is a word part added to a base word, which changes the word's meaning.

**Circle the suffixes -ous, -ist, and -less in the underlined words.
Complete the second sentence with the base word.**

1. Jacques Cousteau was an <u>adventurous</u> man.

   An adventurous person is one who likes ___adventure___.

2. A <u>zoologist</u> is an expert on animal life.

   ___Zoology___ is the study of animals.

3. An aqualung feels <u>weightless</u> when you are underwater.

   You feel the ___weight___ of the aqualung when you are out of the water.

Write two sentences using words with suffixes.

4. ___Answers will vary._____

5. ___Answers will vary._____

Phonics: Words with -ive, -age, -ize
Say the sentences and underline the words that end in -ive, -age, and -ize.

1. Cousteau was a <u>creative</u> person.

2. What <u>percentage</u> of your friends speaks more than one language?

3. Can you <u>recognize</u> the sounds some sea animals make?

4. My partner made <u>positive</u> comments about my work.

5. I didn't <u>realize</u> that the ocean is full of different creatures.

6. When you love the ocean, it's an <u>advantage</u> to live on the coast.

Comprehension: Evaluate Fact and Opinion

- A **fact** is information based on real evidence.
- An **opinion** is information based on what someone believes.

Decide which sentence below is a fact and which is an opinion.
Write *fact* or *opinion*.

1. _____*fact*_____ **a.** Jacques Cousteau read books about pirates, pearl divers, and the ocean.

   _____*opinion*_____ **b.** Books about pirates and the ocean are interesting.

2. _____*opinion*_____ **a.** Swimming with goggles is much better than swimming without goggles.

   _____*fact*_____ **b.** When Jacques Cousteau first swam with goggles, he became even more interested in the ocean.

3. _____*fact*_____ **a.** Jacques Cousteau wanted to design a diving suit that could carry a supply of air.

   _____*opinion*_____ **b.** Early diving suits looked strange.

Write one opinion you have about the topic of underwater exploration.

4. Possible answer: It would be fun to go on an underwater dive in the Caribbean.

Grammar: Subject and Object Pronouns

- A **subject pronoun** takes the place of the subject of a sentence.
- An **object pronoun** takes the place of the object of a sentence.

Tell whether each underlined word is a subject or object pronoun.

1. Sailors travel the oceans, but cannot see submerged objects under <u>them</u>.
   _____object_____.

2. When Jacques Cousteau was young, <u>he</u> loved the ocean. _____subject_____

3. Maria admires <u>him</u>. _____object_____

Name _____

Vocabulary: Word Parts/Suffixes

Suffixes	Meanings
-less	without, not having
-ful	full of, showing
-ist	a person who
-y	having, containing

Write each base word and suffix on the lines. Then define the word.

1. salty _____salt_____ ____y____, _____having or containing salt_____

2. zoologist _____zoo_____ ____ist____, _____a person who studies animals_____

3. hopeful _____hope_____ ____ful____, _____having hope_____

4. weightless _____weight_____ ____less____, _____not having weight_____

Write a sentence using one of the words from above.

5. _____Answers will vary._____

Phonics: Words with *-ive*, *-age*, and *-ize*
Complete each sentence with a new word by adding *-ive*, *-age*, or *-ize* to the word in parentheses.

1. They explored the _____wreckage_____ underwater. (wreck)

2. An _____active_____ person would enjoy exploring underwater. (act)

3. In the future, new people will _____modernize_____ undersea travel. (modern)

4. What _____percentage_____ of the ocean is salt? (percent)

5. What do you find _____attractive_____ about undersea travel? (attract)

Name _____

Comprehension: Evaluate Fact and Opinion
Read the paragraph below. Then, write examples of facts and opinions.

Studying the ocean is one of the best jobs ever. Marine biologists study the plant and animal life in the ocean. Marine biologists also study the effects of pollution on ocean life. Swimming is an important part of their job. Sometimes, marine biologists complete underwater dives. Wearing a wet suit is probably not pleasant.

1. List two facts from the paragraph:

a. Marine biologists study ocean plant and animal life.

b. Sometimes, marine biologists complete underwater dives *or* Marine biologists also study the effects of pollution on ocean life.

2. List two opinions from the paragraph:

a. Studying the ocean is one of the best jobs ever.

b. Wearing a wet suit is probably not pleasant.

Grammar: Subject and Object Pronouns
Rewrite each sentence. Use the correct subject or object pronoun in parentheses.

1. Oceanographers study the oceans that (they/them) love.

   Oceanographers study the oceans that they love.

2. My class went for a boat tour, and (we/us) saw the bay.

   My class went for a boat tour, and we saw the bay.

3. The boat was called the Nautilus. We liked (she/her).

   The boat was called the Nautilus. We liked her.

Name _____

Vocabulary: Dictionary/Homographs

- **Homographs** are words that are spelled the same but have different meanings.

rest	**a.** a part, such as what is left of something
	b. to stop activity and relax
address	**a.** information that gives the location of someone or something (The stress is on the first syllable.)
	b. to direct written or spoken words to a person or group. (The stress is on the second syllable.)

Choose the correct homograph from the box for each sentence.

1. After the game, everyone was tired and needed _____rest_____.

2. I don't know how to find my friend because I don't have his _____address_____.

3. The president will _____address_____ the nation at ten o'clock.

4. Only half of the class went on the field trip; the _____rest_____ didn't.

Use one of the homographs in a sentence of your own.

5. _____Answers will vary._____

Phonics: Prefixes, Suffixes, Base Words

Say the words below. Circle the words with prefixes and suffixes.
Draw lines to separate the circled words into their parts.

1. (in|correct|ly) individual annoy

2. delicate (dis|appoint|ment) danger

3. announce under (un|successful)

Name _____

Comprehension: Compare and Contrast

- To **compare** is to tell how two things are similar.
- To **contrast** is to tell how two things are different.

**Read the details from *A Great Leader: Mary McLeod Bethune*.
Circle *compares* or *contrasts* and complete the sentence.**

1. During the American Civil War, many of the McLeod children were enslaved, but after the war ended, the McLeod children returned to their parents.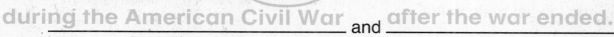

   This sentence compares/(contrasts) the time
   during the American Civil War and _after the war ended._

2. The older McLeod children were born into slavery, but Mary McLeod was born into freedom.

   This sentences compares/(contrasts)
   the older McLeod children and _Mary McLeod._

3. Booker T. Washington opened a school for African Americans, and Mary McLeod also opened a school for African Americans.

   This sentence (compares)/contrasts
   Booker T. Washington and _Mary McLeod._

Grammar: Possessive Pronouns

- A **possessive pronoun** is a pronoun that shows ownership of something.

Rewrite each sentence. Use the correct possessive pronoun.

1. Mary McLeod Bethune worked hard to achieve (her/their) goals.
   Mary McLeod Bethune worked hard to achieve her goals.

2. Mary's parents farmed (my/their) cotton fields.
   Mary's parents farmed their cotton fields.

Name _____

Vocabulary: Dictionary/Homographs
Read the definitions below. Match each homograph with the right definition, or definitions.

1. hasty and careless ___c___   **a.** bass

2. hinder or hold back ___b___   **b.** hamper

3. a type of fish ___a___   **c.** rash

4. a large container ___b___

5. the lowest male voice

   in music ___a___

Write two sentences using a homograph pair. Use a different definition in each sentence.

6. ___Answers will vary._____

Phonics: Prefixes, Suffixes, and Base Words
Read each word below. Write the prefix on the first line, the base word on the second line, and the suffix on the third line.

1. outsider ___out___ ___side___ ___er___

2. incorrectly ___in___ ___correct___ ___ly___

3. unsuccessful ___un___ ___success___ ___ful___

4. disapproval ___dis___ ___approve___ ___al___

5. repayment ___re___ ___pay___ ___ment___

Comprehension: Compare and Contrast
Read the paragraph. Then, explain how the characters compare or contrast with one another.

Omar noticed that his neighbor Mrs. Chang needed help cleaning her yard. When his friend Ali came over, Omar asked him if he wanted to help Mrs. Chang for a few hours. Ali wanted to get to the skate park to meet their other friends. Omar liked going to the skate park, too, but he knew that Mrs. Chang was not able to cut her lawn, pull weeds, and take out the trash all by herself. She had a bad back, but Omar was strong and energetic. Omar helped Mrs. Chang pull weeds and then went to the park to meet his friends. Mrs. Chang decided to use her sewing machine to repair Omar's torn backpack.

1. Compare Omar and Ali.
   Omar and Ali both like the skate park.

2. Contrast Omar and Ali.
   Possible Answer: Omar wanted to help Mrs. Chang, but Ali wanted to go to the skate park.

3. Contrast Omar and Mrs. Chang.
   Possible Answer: Omar is strong and energetic, but Mrs. Chang has a bad back.

4. Compare Omar and Mrs. Chang.
   Omar helped Mrs. Chang with her lawn, and Mrs. Chang helped Omar by repairing his backpack.
   Answers will vary.

Grammar: Possessive Pronouns
Add a possessive pronoun to each sentence.

1. _____ Our _____ town needs help.

2. She needs help for _____ her _____ car.

3. _____ My _____ help will make the situation better.

Name _____

Vocabulary: Analogy/Relationships
- An **analogy** is used to compare the relationships of two pairs of words.

Choose a word from the word bank to complete each of the analogies.

| stage | triathlon | prominent | spectator |

1. Competing is to athlete as watching is to ____spectator____.
2. Winner is to loser as unknown is to ____prominent____.
3. Tree is to leaf as road race is to____stage____.
4. Two is to bicycle as three is to____triathlon____.

Write two sentences using a word from the box in each.

5. ___Answers will vary.___
6. ___Answers will vary.___

Phonics: Vowel Alternation
These pairs of words belong to the same family but are not pronounced the same. Say each pair of words. Circle the vowel that is pronounced differently in each pair.

1. compete - competition
2. nation - national
3. reside - resident
4. wise - wisdom

Name _____

Comprehension: Identify Fact and Opinion

- A **fact** is information based on real evidence.
- An **opinion** is information based on what a person believes.

Read the sentences below. Write *fact* or *opinion* on the line in front of each sentence.

1. _____opinion_____ A cyclist needs to have a good attitude to win.

2. _____fact_____ In 1991, Lance Armstrong was the United States Amateur Champion and a prominent figure in cycling.

3. _____fact_____ The Cooper Institute in Dallas, Texas is a medical research center.

4. _____opinion_____ The type of bicycle that Lance Armstrong rides is one of the best.

Select an opinion from the sentences above. How could the opinion be explained and supported?

5. _Possible answer: Number 4. The type of bicycle that_ _Lance Armstrong rides is lighter, faster, and more_ _cyclists have won races when riding this bicycle._

Grammar: Indefinite Pronouns

- An **indefinite pronoun** is one that does not refer to a specific object.

Underline the indefinite pronoun in each sentence.

1. Everybody can admire Lance Armstrong, an adept bicyclist.

2. Nobody has won the Tour de France more times.

3. Someone has to be very fast to do that.

4. Others would like to do it, too.

Write a sentence of your own with the indefinite pronoun anyone.

5. _Answers will vary._

Name _____

Vocabulary: Analogy/Relationships

Read the analogies below. See the relationship between each pair of words. Complete the analogy by writing one of the words from the word bank.

| adept | collective | exercise | prevail |

1. Spectator is to watch as athlete is to _____exercise_____.

2. Clumsy is to awkward as skilled is to _____adept_____.

3. _____Collective_____ is to group as single is to individual.

4. _____Prevail_____ is to win as fail is to lose.

Write an analogy similar to the analogies above.

5. _____Answers will vary._____

Phonics: Vowel Alternation

Read the words below aloud. Write the base word on the line. Then underline the letter or letters that change sounds when the suffix is added.

1. competition _____compete_____

2. metallic _____metal_____

3. ignition _____ignite_____

4. finality _____final_____

Name _____

Comprehension: Identify Fact and Opinion

Read the paragraph. Then, answer the questions about facts and opinions included in the paragraph.

Bike trails offer a great way to see your state. Many state parks have special bike trails. The maps are easy to follow. If you prepare well, you will prevent problems. Wear a helmet to prevent injuries. Riding your bike is especially fun to do in spring, summer, or autumn. If you ride through a forest during late autumn, you will see the colors of the leaves change on hardwood trees. Riding your bike 10 miles is the same as riding 16.10 kilometers.

1. How did the author tell a fact and an opinion about bike riding in autumn?

   Answer: It is the author's opinion that it is fun to
   ride one's bike in autumn. It is a fact that the
   colors of the leaves change in late autumn.

2. Reread the first and second sentences in the paragraph. Which sentence tells a fact and which tells an opinion?

   Fact - Sentence 2   Opinion - Sentence 1

3. How can the last sentence be proven true?

   The distance of miles and kilometers could be
   measured.

Grammar: Indefinite Pronouns

Write an indefinite pronoun to complete each sentence.

Possible answers:

1. _____Someone_____ went for a bike ride.

2. _____Everyone_____ rode very fast.

3. _____Everyone_____ tried to keep up.

Write a sentence using an indefinite pronoun.

4. _____Answers will vary._____

Name _____

Vocabulary: Homophones
- **Homophones** are words that sound alike, but have different meanings and spellings.

Choose the correct homophone to complete each sentence. Use a dictionary for support.

1. dyeing - dying

   a. We read about _____ dyeing _____ cloth, to make it different colors.

   b. Plants are _____ dying _____ because it hasn't rained for months.

2. eves - eaves

   a. They celebrated on the _____ eves _____, or nights before each holiday.

   b. Birds make nests in the _____ eaves _____.

3. gild - guild

   a. To _____ gild _____ means to paint with the color of gold.

   b. In the Middles Ages, craftsmen with similar interests belonged to a _____ guild _____.

Phonics: Consonant Alternation
- Some words belong to the same **word family** but have consonants that are not pronounced the same.

Say each pair of words. Circle the consonant that is pronounced differently in each pair.

1. office – official

2. critic - criticize

3. public - publicity

4. muscle - muscular

Name _____

Comprehension: Evaluate Author's Perspective

• An **author's perspective** is his or her way of looking at something.

Read the details from *Crafts in the Middle Ages*. Then, write *true* or *false* next to each statement about the author's perspective.

People in the Middle Ages needed to make many visits to craftspeople in order to make clothing.

1. _____true_____ The author's perspective is that it took a lot of work to make every item, such as clothing.

Medieval people loved bright-colored clothing.

2. _____false_____ The author's perspective is that medieval people enjoyed too many luxuries.

By the 1400s, most large towns in Europe had guilds. Guilds, such as a ceramics guild, became very important and powerful.

3. _____false_____ The author's perspective is that guilds did not make a big difference in the lives of medieval people.

Grammar: Pronoun-Verb Agreement, Indefinite Pronouns

A verb must agree with its subject pronoun.
Underline the verb that agrees in each sentence.

1. During the Middle Ages, almost everyone (was/were) a farmer.

2. Someone (makes/make) everything people use.

3. Everything (is/are) deftly made by a different person.

4. Everyone (work/works) together to survive.

Write a sentence of your own with an indefinite pronoun. Circle the indefinite pronoun.

5. _____Answers will vary._____

© Macmillan/McGraw-Hill

Name _____

Vocabulary: Homophones

Read the sentences below. Choose the homophone that completes the sentence.

1. A thatcher can use straw to make the (eaves, eves) of the roof.

   _____eaves_____

2. We found an old (nights, knight's) armor in the building.

   _____knight's_____

3. We found a (peace, piece) of ancient pottery in the tomb. _____piece_____

4. The (blue, blew) ceramic bowl had perfect symmetry. _____blue_____

Write two sentences using a pair of homophones from above, such as *blue* and *blew*.

5. _____Answers will vary._____

6. _____Answers will vary._____

Phonics: Consonant Alternation

Read the words below aloud. Write the base word on the line. Then circle the letter in the base word that changes in sound when the suffix is added.

1. creation _____create_____

2. selection _____select_____

3. publicity _____public_____

4. crumble _____crumb_____

5. rejection _____reject_____

Comprehension: Evaluate Author's Perspective
Draw a line from each detail to the statement about the author's perspective that matches.

In movies, life in a castle seems filled with luxuries and great feasts. However, most castles were built to protect people during attacks. Castles usually included a moat, or ditch. The moat was filled with water to prevent enemies from charging the castle. Without plumbing systems like we have today, the moat became a place to dump everything. Inside, it was cold, damp, and dark. Torches and fireplaces offered the only light and heat.

Details

1. Castles in movies are filled with luxuries.

2. Castles were built to protect people during attacks.

3. The moat was also a place for dumping everything.

Author's Perspective

a. Movies show false ideas about castle life.

b. Dumping is not a clean way to live.

c. A castle was built to be useful, not glamorous.

Grammar: Pronoun-Verb Agreement, Indefinite Pronouns
Underline the indefinite pronoun in parentheses that agrees with the verb.

1. I will get you (anything, many) that you want.

2. (Someone/Each) used it long ago.

3. In arid places, (everyone/something) looks for water supplies.

4. (Most/Nobody) likes to break ceramics.

Write a sentence of your own with an indefinite pronoun. Circle the indefinite pronoun.

5. Answers will vary. _____

Name _____

Vocabulary A **suffix** is a word part that is added to the end of a word. The suffix changes the meaning of the word.

Word	Suffix	Word + Suffix
typical	-ly	typically
special	-ist	specialist
hope	-ful	hopeful

Phonics Adding a **suffix** to the end of a word may change how the word is pronounced. Practice saying the words below aloud.

-ive	*-age*	*-ize*	*-ion*	*-ian*
expense	store	critic	collide	magic
expensive	storage	criticize	collision	magician

Comprehension An **author's purpose** is the author's reason or reasons for writing. An author may try to inform, explain, persuade, or entertain. In the following passage, the author's purpose is to **persuade**. The author writes in an interesting way, so another purpose is to entertain.

> The New York Yankees team is the greatest American baseball team. Over the years, the team has won more games than any other team. The Yankees also have had some of the best baseball players in the world, such as Babe Ruth, Joe DiMaggio, and Mickey Mantle.

Grammar **Indefinite pronouns** take the place of a person, place, or thing that is not specifically named. Review the list of indefinite pronouns below.

anything   another   someone   several   all   something   each
nobody   both   most   neither   anyone   many

Someone hit Tina's car and fled the scene.   **Anyone** can visit this zoo for free.

© Macmillan/McGraw-Hill

Name _____

Match the vocabulary words with their meanings. Then circle the vocabulary words with a suffix.

1. (maturity) __a__   a. adulthood

2. (collective) __d__   b. able

3. hover __c__   c. hang

4. adept __b__   d. combined

Circle the letter of the correct indefinite pronoun for each sentence.

5. Has ____ heard about the demonstration?

   a. all   (b.) anyone   c. the crowd

6. ____ dove into the water but ____ stayed on the beach.

   (a.) Few, many   b. People, he   c. Guillermo, that girl

Circle the errors with pronouns and errors with *they, their,* and *they're.* Write your answers on the line below.

   In the late 1950s, Homer Hickam was determined to build a rocket after (him) watched the first satellite fly into space. He was from a West Virginia mining town, and (their) father had different ideas for (her) future. Homer studied physics and experimented with rockets. He often worked alone and almost blew (themselves) up. Yet, (they) made a successful launch in front of everyone in town. His friends and neighbors cheered for him. (They're) support was very important to Homer.

7. he 8. his 9. his 10. himself 11. he 12. Their

What is the author's purpose?

To inform the reader about Homer Hickam; to entertain the reader with an interesting story.

© Macmillan/McGraw-Hill

Phonics: Suffixes
Read the text. Circle the words with suffixes -ible, -able, -sion, -less.
Read the text again. Then answer the following questions.

Jacques Cousteau was a remarkable oceanographer. He studied the wonders of the seas through exploration. He spent countless hours making films underwater. He wanted to make the deep ocean visible to people who might never see it. He wanted to educate them in an enjoyable way.

Viewers throughout the world received an education about the ocean by watching his weekly television program. His methods of persuasion encouraged more people to explore the ocean and want to protect it. If you would see Cousteau's films, you would surely want to become an undersea explorer.

Comprehension: Author's Purpose, Fact and Opinion

1. Describe the author's purpose.

   The author's purpose is to tell people about the work of Jacques Cousteau.

2. Draw and complete a Fact and Opinion Chart for this text.

Fact	Opinion

   Fact—He was an oceanographer; he studied the wonders of the sea through exploration; he had a weekly television show.
   Opinion—He was remarkable; you would want to become an undersea explorer.

© Macmillan/McGraw-Hill

Name _____

Vocabulary
Read each sentence. Circle the letter of the word that best completes the sentence.

1. Ma Lee was not sure what she wanted to write her report about, so she decided to ask her teacher for ____.

   a. inspections   **b.** paper   **c.** predictions   **(d.)** guidance

2. At first, Mercedes was afraid to go underwater, but after a few minutes, she ____ her head.

   (a.) submerged   **b.** elevated

   c. subtracted   **d.** absorbed

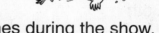

3. Movie theaters now ____ the use of cell phones during the show.

   a. interpret   **(b.)** prohibit   **c.** explain   **d.** encourage

4. The team scored a touchdown and the ____ cheered.

   a. inspectors   **b.** subscribers   **(c.)** spectators   **d.** transporters

5. Aidan learned how to make a vase in ____ class.

   a. engineering   **b.** sewing   **(c.)** ceramics   **d.** mechanical drawing

6. Someone who studies animals is a ____.

   a. botanist   **b.** biologist   **c.** chemist   **(d.)** zoologist

Phonics: Suffixes
Circle the word that does not have a suffix in each group.

7. collision   (hover)   storage

8. (guide)   criticize   maturity

Grammar: Indefinite Pronouns, Pronoun-Verb Agreement
Choose the correct indefinite pronouns to complete each sentence. Circle the letter of the answer.

1. Pierre thinks that _____ who competes in the Tour de France, deserves respect from _____.

   a. anyone, everyone   **b.** Maria, Dominique's family

2. _____ maneuvered the obstacle course well, but _____ completed it.

   a. Some, few   **b.** All the athletes, only Frank

3. _____ is perfect.

   a. Both   **b.** Anita   **c.** Nobody

4. Are you going to give that to _____?

   a. the students   **b.** somebody   **c.** Juan

Choose the correct verb that agrees with the pronoun in each sentence. Circle the letter of the answer.

5. When submerged, he _____ weightless in the water.

   a. feels   **b.** feel

6. They _____ a safe boat that they _____ to explore the ocean.

   a. has, uses   **b.** have, use

7. She _____ adults how to make pottery, and she _____ her job.

   a. teaches, loves   **b.** teach, love

**Editing: Correct Use of *they*, *their*, and *they're* and
Pronoun Agreement**
Read the story. Look for errors in using *they, their,* and
they're. Find pronouns that are used incorrectly. Circle
the errors and write the corrections on the lines.

Jesse Owens

1. _____their_____   African American athletes like
Jesse Owens experienced many
obstacles in they're careers. Jesse

2. _____he_____   participated in the Olympic games in Berlin,
Germany, in 1936, but they was treated poorly.
Jesse won four

3. _____his_____   gold medals and the spectators cheered, but the
German leader, Hitler, refused to shake their hand
because he was black.

4. _____there_____   When Jesse returned to the U.S., he met
obstacles their. Companies did not ask African
Americans to

5. _____there_____   endorse their products. Jesse felt that they're had to
be another way. He started a public relations firm,

6. _____he_____   and gave talks all over the country. In 1976,
President Ford awarded Jesse the Medal of Freedom
because they fought to prove to the world that
African Americans belonged in the world of athletics.

Comprehension: Authors' Purpose, Compare and Contrast

1. Why did the author write this text? Tell more than one reason.

   to inform about Jesse Owens; to persuade that it is
   wrong to treat people unfairly

2. Compare how Hitler treated Jesse to how President Ford treated him later.

   Hitler treated him with disrespect. President Ford
   honored him.

Vocabulary: Word Parts/Build Word Families

Underline the words that belong to the same family as the word on the left. Circle the prefixes and suffixes in the words you underline.

1. legal   **a.** logical   **b.** illegal   **c.** legality   **d.** legend

2. comfort   **a.** concern   **b.** concert   **c.** comfortable   **d.** discomfort

3. treat   **a.** treatment   **b.** trait   **c.** mistreated   **d.** trainer

4. migrant   **a.** mention   **b.** migration   **c.** immigrant   **d.** meager

List two words that form a family. Use one of the words in a sentence.

5. _____, _____

Answers will vary.

_____

Phonics: Homophones

- **Homophones** are words that sound the same but have different meanings and spellings.

Underline the homophones. Then answer each question with the correct homophone.

1. **a.** I need a hanger for my coat.

   b. We saw a small plane going into a hangar.

   Which homophone refers to hanging clothes? _____

   hanger

2. **a.** Honesty is the most important principle for me.

   b. What are the principal parts of the verb to take?

   Which homophone means the same as main? _____

   principal

3. **a.** Take this medicine to lessen the pain.

   b. We will have a quiz after we finish this lesson.

   Which homophone means the same as reduce? _____

   lessen

Name _____

Comprehension: Evaluate Author's Purpose

- The **author's purpose** is the author's reason for writing.

Answer the questions about the author's purpose in
Micaela's New Friend.

1. Why did the author write that Micaela didn't want to get up the morning of her first day of middle school, even though her mother uttered her name from the kitchen several times?

   Possible Answer: The author wanted to show that Micaela was nervous about the day ahead.

2. Why did the author write that Micaela noticed that her new school was bigger than her old school?

   Possible Answer: The author wanted to show that the school's size was making Micaela more nervous.

3. Why did the author write that the last week before Micaela moved, she spent every day with her friend Mariana?

   Possible Answer: The author wanted to show how close the two friends were.

Grammar: Adjectives and Demonstrative Adjectives

- An **adjective** is a word that describes a noun.
- A **demonstrative adjective** refers to where a noun is (*this*, *that*, *these*).

Underline each adjective once. Underline each demonstrative adjective twice.

1. This girl, Micaela, was nervous.

2. Micaela wondered what that new school would be like.

3. These happy students like going to school.

Vocabulary: Word Parts/Build Word Families
Read each word below. Write two words in its word family.
Use a dictionary for support.
Possible answers:

1. legal _____illegal_____ _____legally_____

2. treat _____mistreat_____ _____treated_____

3. migrant _____migration_____ _____migrating_____

4. friend _____friendship_____ _____friendly_____

Write a sentence using one of the word family words from above.

5. _____Answers will vary._____

Phonics: Homophones
Read each word below. Write a homophone
of the word on the line.

1. principle _____principal_____

2. pane _____pain_____

3. vein _____vain_____

4. weak _____week_____

PRINCIPAL

Name _____

Comprehension: Evaluate Author's Purpose
Read the paragraph below. Then, label each statement *true* or *false*.

My brother is the best tennis coach. Whether I know it or not, every time we step on the court, it's another lesson. John knows how to get me to move quickly without yelling. He never yells, but simply encourages. Lots of times I have to pick up all the yellow tennis balls scattered across the court, but I don't mind. We pretend we are famous players, too, and practice our victory shots. It's good practice playing with my brother.

1. __true__ The author wrote this to describe the best tennis coach.

2. __false__ The author wrote that John does not yell at him to explain that John only yells if he is playing with a friend.

3. __false__ The author wrote about having to pick up all the tennis balls to show that John can be mean sometimes.

4. __true__ The author wrote about pretending to be famous tennis players to show that John was creative.

Grammar: Adjectives and Demonstrative Adjectives
Complete each sentence with an adjective and a demonstrative adjective. Possible answers:

1. _____This_____ girl had a _____smart_____ friend.

2. _____This_____ advice was _____wise_____.

3. _____These_____ ideas were always _____useful_____.

4. _____That_____ mentor was _____helpful_____.

Write a sentence of your own with an adjective and a demonstrative adjective.

5. Answers will vary. _____

Name _____

Vocabulary: Word Parts/Latin Roots

- A **Latin root** is a root word in English that originates from Latin. Latin roots help you figure out the meaning of words.

Use the Latin roots shown to find the meaning of each underlined word.

> **ject =** to throw, throw away, throw down
>
> **ciens, scire, scient =** to know, have knowledge

1. Stacey was <u>dejected</u> because she thought she had to give up playing soccer.

   a. upbeat **b.** excited **c.** feeling down **d.** content

2. The captain was <u>conscious</u> his teammates were depending on him for victory.

   a. hopeful **b.** aware **c.** pretending **d.** saying

3. My friends <u>rejected</u> my idea for a science project.

   a. liked **b.** copied **c.** acknowledged **d.** turned down

Phonics: Latin Roots

Say each word on the left. Refer to the chart on the right and underline the Latin root in each word.

1. herbivorous

2. unscientific

3. satisfied

4. arboretum

5. vital

Latin Root	Meaning
arbor	tree
herba	grass
satis	enough
scient	to have knowledge
vita	life

Name _____

Comprehension: Compare and Contrast

- To **compare** is to find the similarities between things.
- To **contrast** is to find the differences between things.

Write *compare* or *contrast* to describe each detail from *The Big Decision*.

1. ___compare___ Stacey and her three best friends were going to the same middle school.

2. ___contrast___ Stacey, Mandy, and Darrell were taking Spanish class, but Luis was taking French.

3. ___compare___ Stacey and Lila were both in Mr. Ling's English class.

4. ___contrast___ Stacey did not know whether to participate in soccer or the newspaper, but her friends were certain they wanted to play soccer.

Grammar: Articles

- An **article** is a word used to refer to a noun and its function.
- A **definite article** (*the*) is specific.
- An **indefinite article** (*a*, *an*) is not specific.

Underline the article in each sentence.

1. The school newspaper met on Tuesdays.

2. Each student had a job.

3. Stacey was an eager reporter, who anticipated great stories.

Write a sentence with an article. Circle the article.

4. ___Answers will vary.___ _____

Name _____

Vocabulary: Word Parts/Latin Roots

Read the sentences below. Use the Latin roots as clues to the meanings of the words, and choose the word in parentheses that fits the sentence. Rewrite each sentence using the correct Latin root word.

Latin Roots

ject = throw	**struct** = build	**port** = carry

1. He (dejectedly, instruction) threw his arms down in defeat.

   He dejectedly threw his arms down in defeat.

2. The (project, portable) radio was easy to carry.

   The portable radio was easy to carry.

3. We are going to (construct, inject) a building in five days.

   We are going to construct a building in five days.

4. We are going to bring (reject, imports) into our country.

   We are going to bring imports into our country.

Phonics: Latin Roots

Read the words below. Write the three word parts on the lines. Then circle the Latin root.

1. inspector _____in_____ _____spect_____ _____or_____

2. contractor _____con_____ _____tract_____ _____or_____

3. description _____de_____ _____scrip_____ _____tion_____

4. imported _____im_____ _____port_____ _____ed_____

Comprehension: Compare and Contrast
Write sentences that compare or contrast ideas from the paragraph.

The students at Ralph Waldo Emerson Middle School were planning for their future. Making plans and having goals is smart thinking. Sarah wants to be a doctor or a nurse. She volunteers at a hospital. Jafar loves music. He wants to become a musician. He practices his instrument every day and tries to learn as much as he can. Amelia likes music and working with children. She spends time learning more about music and how to work with children. She volunteers at a program for young children.

1. Compare Sarah and Amelia.
   Sarah and Amelia both do volunteer work.

2. Contrast Sarah and Jafar. Sarah wants to be a doctor, and Jafar wants to be a musician.

3. Compare Amelia and Jafar.
   Amelia and Jafar both like music.

4. How might Amelia, Jafar, and Sarah be like other middle school students?
   Like other students, they want to spend their time doing the things they like.

Grammar: Articles
Complete each sentence with an article.

1. Susan had _____the_____ biggest problem.

2. It was _____an_____ ordeal, or harsh experience.

3. She had to think of __an or the__ answer.

4. _____The_____ ideas she had were good.

Write a sentence with an article. Circle the article.

5. _Answers will vary._____

Name _____

Vocabulary: Word Parts/Greek Roots

- **Greek roots** are word parts that come from the Greek language.

Refer to the chart and choose the word to complete each sentence.

Word	Greek Root	Meaning
chronological	chrono	time
automobile	auto	self
geology	geo	earth
democracy	demos	people

1. The science that studies such subjects as rocks and volcanoes
   is called ___geology___.

2. Before the ___automobile___ was invented, people traveled in horse-drawn carriages.

3. In a ___democracy___, the people elect their representatives.

4. Write the main events in your life in ___chronological___ order.

Use a word with a Greek root to write a sentence.

5. ___Answers will vary._____

Phonics: Greek Roots

Say each word on the left. Refer to the chart on the right and underline the Greek root in each word.

1. microscope

2. hemisphere

3. photosynthesis

4. thermometer

5. pentagon

Greek Root	Meaning
hemi	half
micro	small
penta	five
photo	light
therm	heat

© Macmillan/McGraw-Hill

Comprehension: Identify Techniques of Persuasion

- Authors sometimes write their feelings about a subject, or **opinions**, instead of **facts**. It is important for readers to know the difference.

For each idea from *Making Money at the Treasury* write *fact* or *opinion*.

1. _____fact_____ During World War II, original copies of the Declaration of Independence and other important documents were stored at Fort Knox.

2. _____opinion_____ The Treasury Building is as important as the White House and the Capitol Building.

3. _____fact_____ The Secretary of the Treasury is in charge of all 20 units of the Department of the Treasury.

Grammar: Adjectives that Compare

- **Comparative adjectives** compare two things.
- **Superlative adjectives** compare more than two things.

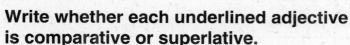

Write whether each underlined adjective is comparative or superlative.

1. The IRS is the <u>largest</u> branch of the Treasury. _____superlative_____

2. The Treasury's economists work to make trade <u>easier</u>. _____comparative_____

3. Some dollar bills last <u>longer</u> than others. _____comparative_____

Write a sentence with an adjective that compares.

4. _____Answers will vary._____

Name _____

Vocabulary: Word Parts/Greek Roots

Read the sentences below. The box shows Greek roots and their meanings. Use the Greek roots in the box as clues to help you figure out the words in parentheses. Rewrite the sentence using the correct Greek root word.

Greek Roots

auto = self	**bio** = life
graph = writing	**gram** = thing written

1. She made a lot of money writing her (autobiography, biology).
   She made a lot of money writing her autobiography.

2. She wanted the star's (graphic, autograph).
   She wanted the star's autograph.

3. His love of animals led him to study (telegram, biology).
   His love of animals led him to study biology.

4. He wrote a (telegram, biotic). He wrote a telegram.

Phonics: Greek Roots

Read the words below. Write the word parts on the lines. Then circle the Greek root you know.

1. syn̄chronize _____syn_____ _____chron_____ _____ize_____

2. (photo)graph _____photo_____ _____graph_____

3. (therm)al _____therm_____ _____al_____

4. (chron)ic _____chron_____ _____ic_____

Comprehension: Techniques of Persuasion
Read the paragraph. Then, identify the facts and opinions.

Making food from recipes is a good way to save money. Home-cooked food usually tastes better than pre-made food. Pre-made products usually cost more than the ingredients needed to make the meal from a recipe. Once you have a bag of flour, water, and some yeast, you can make several loaves of bread. Once pre-made food is eaten, you have to return to the store to buy more. In addition, cooking is a fun and relaxing activity.

1. Name two facts from the passage.

   Possible answers: Making food from recipes saves money. When you have the ingredients, you can make several loaves of bread.

2. Name two opinions from the passage.

   Possible answers: Home-cooked food tastes better than pre-made food. Cooking is fun and relaxing.

Grammar: Adjectives that Compare
Complete each sentence with the comparative or superlative form of the adjective in parentheses.

1. Alexander Hamilton was the _____earliest_____ Secretary of the Treasury. (early)

2. Economists still think his ideas are _____wiser_____ than others. (wise)

3. Fort Knox is one of the _____safest_____ places in the country. (safe)

Name _____

Vocabulary: Thesaurus/Dictionary/Antonyms

- **Antonyms** are pairs of words with opposite meanings.

Choose an antonym for each word given. Use the word you choose in a sentence.

1. close

   a. tranquil   **b.** vacant   **c.** new   **d.** far

   Answers will vary. _____

2. decreasing

   a. ending   **b.** invading   **c.** increasing   **d.** wanting

   Answers will vary. _____

3. unknown

   a. uninformed   **b.** unusual   **c.** famous   **d.** fancy

   Answers will vary. _____

Phonics: Suffixes -*able*, -*ible*

Say the sentences below and underline the words with the suffix -*able* or -*ible*. Write the words in the chart that follows.

1. Our home team had a terrible baseball season.

2. Why are some baseball cards more valuable than others?

3. There are lots of tickets available for today's game.

4. My friend was barely audible when he called me from the stadium.

Words ending in -*able*	Words ending in -*ible*
valuable	terrible
available	audible

Name _____

Comprehension: Make Judgments

- A **judgment** is an opinion you make after thinking carefully.

Use what you know and these ideas from
***All About Baseball* to make each judgment.**

1. Baseball was the perfect game for people who lived in
   small towns and worked on farms.

   Judgment: _Possible answer: It makes sense that a_
   game that required a big field began in rural areas.

2. The story that tells that the idea that Abner Doubleday invented baseball
   is a myth.

   Judgment: _Possible answer: It would be impossible to_
   find the inventors of many games.

3. Honus Wagner stole more than 700 bases.

   Judgment: _Possible answer: Wagner was an_
   unbelievable player.

Grammar: Comparing with *More* and *Most*

- For words with two or more syllables, add the word *more* to create a
  comparative adjective.
- Add the word *most* to create a **superlative adjective**.

Choose the correct word in parentheses, and underline it.

1. In the 1950s, baseball had been the (more/<u>most</u>) popular American sport
   for 100 years.

2. Ty Cobb has the (more/<u>most</u>) impressive batting average of all time.

3. He played (<u>more</u>/most) instinctively than other players.

Write a sentence with *more* and an adjective.

4. _Answers will vary._

Name _____

Vocabulary: Thesaurus/Dictionary/Antonyms

Rewrite each sentence with the correct antonym to replace the word in parentheses.

| decreasing | dilapidated | impossible | shakily |

1. That baseball card is (increasing) in value.
   That baseball card is decreasing in value.
   _____

2. He (steadily) gave me his coin collection.
   He shakily gave me his coin collection.
   _____

3. Collecting all the cards was (possible).
   Collecting all the cards was impossible.
   _____

4. The stamps he collects are (like new).
   The stamps he collects are dilapidated.
   _____

Phonics: Suffixes -able and -ible

Write a new word on the line by adding either -able or -ible to each word.

1. value ___valuable___

2. believe ___believable___

3. reverse ___reversible___

4. convert ___convertible___

Name _____

Comprehension: Make Judgments
Answer each question with a judgment.

The world record holder for the largest collection of chewing gum lives in London, England. Steve Fletcher began collecting chewing gum packets in 1980. He hasn't stopped yet. When he travels, he buys gum to add to his collection. Mr. Fletcher has packets of gum from over 25 different countries. He is a Guinness World record holder. A Guinness World record is an award for doing something no one else has done or having something no one else has.

1. Explain what it means to have a world record.

   A world record means __You have something no one else__ __has or have done something no one else has done.__

2. Why do you think Steve Fletcher began this collection? Explain.

   __Possible Answer: He liked the look of gum packets.__

3. Why would the gum packages from around the world be interesting?

   __Possible Answer: Different languages on the__ __package; different symbols or size.__

Grammar: Comparing with *more* and *most*
Complete each sentence with *more* or *most* and an adjective.

1. This stamp is the ___most___ ___dilapidated___ in my collection.

2. This Guatemalan stamp is ___Possible answer: more___ ___precious___ than that stamp.

3. My album is the ___Possible answer: most___ ___important___ thing I own.

Name _____

Vocabulary: Context Clues/Examples
**Circle clues that will help you figure out the meaning
of the underlined words.**

1. César Chávez's mother had strong <u>convictions</u>. Convictions are (principles or strong beliefs) a person has.

2. Campesinos were <u>suspicious</u> of one another and this (lack of trust) kept them from working together for a common purpose.

3. Chávez was convincing and <u>persistent</u>, (not a person who gives up) after the second or third try.

4. When you saw the crowds around César Chávez, it was <u>evident</u>, or (clear), that he had many followers.

Write a sentence with one of the underlined words.

5. Answers will vary. _____

Phonics: Suffixes -*ant*, -*ent*, -*ance*, and -*ence*
- Words ending in -**ant** and -**ent** are adjectives.
- Words ending in -**ance** and -**ence** are nouns.

Say each pair of words and circle the suffixes. Copy the words in the chart.

1. eleg(ant) – eleg(ance)
2. intellig(ent) – intellig(ence)
3. import(ant) – import(ance)
4. evid(ent) – evid(ence)

Adjectives ending in -*ant*, -*ent*	Nouns ending in -*ance*, -*ence*
elegant	elegance
intelligent	intelligence
important	importance
evident	evidence

© Macmillan/McGraw-Hill

Name _____

Comprehension: Summarize

- To **summarize** is to tell the main facts about something.

Place a check mark next to the sentences that could be included in a summary about *César Chávez*.

1. ____√____ César Chávez and his family were migrant workers.

2. ____√____ The Chávez family wanted to change the terrible conditions of the migrant workers.

3. _____ During the 1966 march, led by Chávez, workers sang songs like *Viva la Causa* (*Long Live the Cause*).

4. ____√____ Because of his convictions, César Chávez helped organize the National Farm Workers Association (NFWA).

5. _____ The contracts that were written expired, or ended, in three years.

Grammar: Comparing with *good* and *bad*

- *Good* and *bad* have irregular forms for the **comparative** and the **superlative**.

Underline the correct word in parentheses.

1. The Depression was not a (good, worst, best) time for farmers.

2. Conditions were (bad, worse, worst) in the cities than on farms.

3. Because of César Chávez's convictions, farmworkers' lives are (good, better, best) today than they were before.

Write a sentence with the word *worst*.

4. Answers will vary. _____

Name _____

Vocabulary: Context Clues/Examples

Read the following sentences. Write the word or phrase in each sentence that is a context clue for the underlined word.

1. Her voice <u>resonated</u> like thunder in the halls. __like thunder__

2. <u>Remedies</u>, like new contracts, were not enough.
   __like new contracts__

3. He fought for his <u>convictions</u>, like justice for all people.
   __like justice for all people__

4. Acts of <u>defiance</u>, like sitting in the front of the bus, occurred during the 1950s.
   __like sitting in the front of the bus__

Write a sentence using an example in it. Underline the word that the example describes.

5. __Answers will vary.__ _____

Phonics: Suffixes -ant, -ent, -ance, -ence

Read each word below aloud. Rewrite the word so that it has an -ance or -ence ending.

1. important __importance__

2. independent __independence__

3. persistent __persistence__

4. defiant __defiance__

5. nonviolent __nonviolence__

Name _____

Comprehension: Summarize
Answer the questions to summarize the paragraph.

John Steinbeck wanted the world to know about the working conditions of the migrant workers living in California during the 1930s and 1940s. First, Steinbeck wrote newspaper articles describing the unfair conditions on farms. Later, he wrote novels that described, in detail, the lives of migrant workers. Steinbeck was able to communicate the injustices that many people experienced. For his readers, the novels helped them to change their attitudes and encouraged more people to work for fair working conditions for all people.

1. What years and location did John Steinbeck write about?

a. _the 1930s and 1940s._____

b. _California farms_____

2. What group of people was described in Steinbeck's novels?

_migrant workers_____

3. How did Steinbeck's novels affect his readers?

The novels helped to change readers' attitudes and

encouraged them to work for fair working

conditions for all people.

Grammar: Comparing with *Good* and *Bad*
Complete each sentence with the correct form of *good* or *bad*.

1. Justice is ____better____ than oppression.

2. Peace for all people is the ____best____ situation.

3. Some leaders inspire us to lead ____better____ lives than before.

Write a sentence of your own with the word *worst*.

4. _Answers will vary._____

Vocabulary Words that have opposite meanings are called **antonyms**. A thesaurus lists many antonyms.

    antonyms   *legally* is the opposite of *illegally*
                    misery is the opposite of *delight*

Phonics Some English words have **Latin** and **Greek roots**. Read the words in the chart below.

Latin roots	tract	spect	port	scrib
Meaning	drag, draw	look	carry	write
English words	subtract contract	prospect respect	import export	describe prescribe

Greek root	photo	chron
Meaning	light	time
English words	photograph photographer	chronology chronicle

Comprehension A **fact** is information that is true. An **opinion** is information based on what someone believes or feels.

    Fact   Toni Morrison was the first black woman to receive the Nobel Prize in Literature.

    Opinion   Toni Morrison's book, *Beloved*, is her best novel.

Grammar A **demonstrative adjective** is an adjective that points out a specific thing, person, or concept. The most common demonstrative adjectives are this, that, these, and those.

    We need to discuss a solution for **that** problem.
    Those rafters are dilapidated.
    Periodically, **these** flowers bloom.
    Many changes have occurred during **this** decade.

Name _____

Match the vocabulary words with their antonyms or opposite meanings.

1. wrath ___d___   **a.** last performance of an actor or actress

2. victorious ___c___   **b.** hidden

3. evident ___b___   **c.** defeated

4. debut ___a___   **d.** happiness

Choose the correct form of comparison to complete each sentence.

5. Rico was ____ excited about watching a live auction than Estrella, but Sergio was the ____ excited of all.

   a. more, most   **b.** most, more

6. Catrina thinks that she is the ____ basketball player on the team, but Sonya thinks that she is a ____ player than Catrina.

   a. best, better   **b.** better, best

Read the story. Circle errors in capitalization and the incorrect use of *bad, worse,* and *worst*. Fill in your answers in the lines below.

Dr. abello looked kindly at Emilio sneezing in the examining room. She spoke softly, but sternly. "Your cold is very bad. It is the worse one I've seen all year! Do you want it to become worst and miss out on your sports?" Emilio answered, "I don't feel too worse. I just *sound* awful! You should hear my brother Antonio. He sounds even worser than I do!" Dr. Abello smiled. "Well, I will see your brother later. I will fill out this prescription. Now, be sure to take the medicine."

7. Abello 8. worst 9. worse 10. bad 11. worse

Name _____

Phonics: Homophones
**Read the story. Circle the homophone pairs in the story.
Read the story a second time. Then answer the questions.**

Gaspar looked dejected. "What's wrong?" asked his brother Tony.
"I'm so weak in algebra, I'm never going to pass!" answered Gaspar.
"There are many things you can do to improve, Gaspar, but it will take
up some of your free time," replied Tony.

Gaspar tried what Tony suggested. Every week, he
studied harder and he asked his teacher to write extra
practice questions for him. Every time his assignments
were due, he turned them in on time. Most of his answers
were right. One day, Tony asked, "How are your algebra
tests now?"

Gaspar smiled. "They're much better," he said.

Comprehension: Author's Purpose, Main Idea

1. What was the author's purpose in writing the text?

   Possible answers - to entertain, to show that
   studying hard will improve your grades

2. Draw and complete a Main Idea Web for this story.

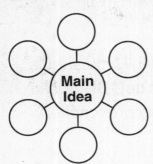

Center circle—how to improve
in algebra
Outer circles—use free time to
study, ask your teacher to write
more examples for you, get
assignments done on time

Vocabulary
Read each sentence. Circle the letter of the word that best completes the sentence.

1. Sixteen students signed up for the foot race, and so Marina decided to _____ as well.

   a. participate   **b.** win   **c.** help   **d.** share

2. The new actress had a stunning Broadway _____ in a New York theater.

   a. reception   **b.** retirement   **c.** celebration   **d.** debut

3. Antonio's _____ as a fine guitar player grew after the concert.

   a. reputation   **b.** equipment

   c. stereotype   **d.** predicaments

Match each vocabulary word with its antonym.

4. decreasing __c__   **a.** intact

5. beautiful __b__   **b.** ugly

6. dilapidated __a__   **c.** increasing

Phonics: Greek and Latin Root Words
Circle the word that has the Greek or Latin root *spect* or *chron* in each group.

7. evident   decade   prospect

8. ruptured   chronicle   encounter

Name _____

Grammar: Comparing with *more* and *most*, Comparing with *good* and *bad*, articles *the*, *a*, and *an*
Circle the letter of the pair of correct adjectives to complete each sentence.

1. Santiago's tree house was the ____ dilapidated in the neighborhood.

   a. more   **b.** most

2. Ana had a ____ extensive collection of cards than Rico, but Marcus had the ____ extensive collection of all.

   a. most, more   **b.** more, most

Circle the letter of the correct forms of comparison using *good* or *bad* to complete each sentence.

3. The old rafters in my barn are ____, but the ones in Eric's barn are ____ because some fell down.

   a. bad, worse

   b. worst, worse

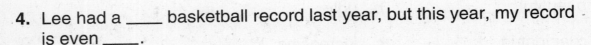

4. Lee had a ____ basketball record last year, but this year, my record is even ____.

   a. good, better   **b.** better, best

Circle the letter of the correct article to complete each sentence.

5. I have ____ mentor who is helping me choose ____ career.

   a. the, the   **b.** a, a   **c.** the, a

6. ____ economist might know why gasoline prices rise and fall.

   a. A   **b.** An

7. My friend Jinwon is ____ immigrant from ____ country of Korea.

   a. an, the   **b.** the, a

Editing: Using Irregular Comparative Forms: *bad*, *good*;
Capitalize Proper Nouns
Look for errors in the use of the comparative forms
of *good* and *bad* and in capitalization. Circle the errors
and make the corrections on the lines.

Mai's Apple Pie

Mai carefully takes an apple pie out of the oven. Yee cuts a slice and
tries it. She makes a terrible face and spits it out.

1. _____worst_____ **Yee:** Excuse me, Mai. I have to be honest. This pie
tastes awful. It's the worse pie I've ever tasted!

2. _____Aunt_____ **Mai:** How can you say that? I'm sure it's good. I used
my aunt Kia's recipe. She's a professional baker and
my mentor. I followed the directions exactly!

3. _____aunt's_____ **Yee:** Let's figure out what's wrong. Are you sure this
is your Aunt's recipe?

4. _____bad_____ **Mia:** I wonder what I did to make it so worse?

5. _good or better_ **Yee:** Look at this bag, Mai. You used salt instead of
sugar! I'll help you make a best pie.

6. _____Your_____ your next pie will be delicious.

Comprehension: Summarize, Make Judgments

1. What is the story about? Summarize it.

   Mai bakes a pie. Yee tries it and tells Mai it's
   terrible. Yee discovers that Mai used salt instead of
   sugar and offers to help her make another.

2. Would you want Yee to be your partner on a class project? Why or
   why not?

   Yes, because she would offer criticism, good

   suggestions, and help.

Name _____

Vocabulary: Word Parts/Greek Roots

• A **Greek root** is a word part that comes from the Greek language.

Choose the word to complete each sentence.

Greek Roots

phil, phile = lover	**meter, metr** = measure
biblio, bibl = book	**sophia** = wisdom

1. A philosopher can be described as a person who

   a. has a soul.

   b. loves wisdom.

   c. cares for nature.

   d. likes mind games.

2. A bibliophile can be described as a person who

   a. studies small parts of the brain.

   b. likes to measure.

   c. loves books.

   d. has studied great minds.

Phonics: Greek and Latin Prefixes

Say each word on the left. Refer to the chart on the right and underline the Greek or Latin prefix in each word.

1. renaissance

2. polygon

3. intermediate

4. cooperate

5. postpone

Prefix	Meaning
co	together
inter	between
poly	many
post	coming after
re	again

Name _____

Comprehension: Make Generalizations

- A **generalization** is a statement that can apply to many situations.

Read each generalization. Write a detail from *Michelangelo's Ceiling* that supports each generalization.

1. **Generalization:** Michelangelo will always be remembered as a great painter.

   Detail: _Possible answer: He lived in the 1500s and is still famous._

2. **Generalization:** The Renaissance was the most creative time period in history.

   Detail: _Possible answer: Rich families supported artists._

3. **Generalization:** Many people go to museums to see Michelangelo's paintings.

   Detail: _Possible answer: People from around the world visit museums that have paintings by Michelangelo._

Grammar: Adverbs

- An **adverb** is a word that describes a verb, an adjective, or another adverb.

Underline the adverb in each sentence. Circle the verb, adjective, or other adverb that it describes.

1. The pope often commissioned Michelangelo for artwork.

2. Michelangelo worked extremely hard on the Sistine Chapel.

3. Today the Sistine Chapel is beautifully preserved.

Write a sentence with an adverb.

4. _Answers will vary._

Vocabulary: Word Parts/Greek Roots
Read the Greek roots below. Choose the correct Greek root
word in parentheses to complete each sentence.

Greek Roots

path = feeling	**poli** = city
mech = machine	**photo** = light

1. His paintings were filled with (metropolis, pathos), or sad feeling.

   __pathos__

2. His frescos are more vivid than a (photograph, mechanism).

   __photograph__

3. His sculpting was not (mechanical, general), but fluid and graceful.

   __mechanical__

Phonics: Greek and Latin Prefixes
Choose the correct word in parentheses that
completes each sentence.

1. Coleridge and Wordsworth (cooperated, co-worker)

   with each other to write *Lyrical Ballads*. __cooperated__

2. His (procession, profession) was writing poetry. __profession__

3. He (postdated, postponed) his trip because of the work. __postponed__

4. When the artist was young, his (submersions, submissions) to

   the well-known magazine were rejected. __submissions__

Comprehension: Make Generalizations
Read the paragraph. Then, place a check mark next to the generalizations below.

Easter Island has a lot of volcanic rock. The people who lived on this Polynesian island were sculptors. They carved giant stone statues that have lasted for hundreds of years. Their statues are of giant heads and shoulders. Some statues are over 45 feet tall. It is not known why the islanders carved huge statues. Archaeologists continue to study and look for answers.

____✓____ Most sculptors live near large quantities of rock.

_____ The giant stone statues have lasted a long time.

_____ Archaeologists continue to study Easter Island statues.

____✓____ Most archaeologists dream of a big discovery.

____✓____ Statues are usually tall and huge.

Grammar: Adverbs
Write the correct adverb for each sentence.

Adverbs

| forever | quickly | especially |

1. During the Renaissance, artists ____especially____ loved elaborate design.

2. They worked ____quickly____ on the frescoes.

3. Some of the frescoes found in churches will last ____forever____.

Write a sentence with an adverb.

4. ____Answers will vary.____

© Macmillan/McGraw-Hill

Name _____

Vocabulary: Thesaurus/Dictionary/Synonyms

- Synonyms may have the same definition, or denotation, but different connotations. **Connotation** is the idea or feeling created by a word.

Read the denotation and connotation of each word below.

> *glumly*
> **denotation:** in an unresponsive manner
> **connotation:** acting in a discouraged, depressed way
>
> *sulkily*
> **denotation:** in an unresponsive manner
> **connotation:** acting in a resentful, unpleasant way

Complete the sentences with either *glumly* or *sulkily* based on the context.

1. My partner and I tried hard but couldn't solve the math problem, so we

   looked _____glumly_____ at each other.

2. My younger brother is acting _____sulkily_____ because he can't play
   on my computer.

Phonics: Absorbed Prefixes

Read the word parts below aloud. Combine the prefix and root to create a new word. Notice the spelling changes.

1. in + mobile _____immobile_____

2. ad + count _____account_____

3. con + respond _____correspond_____

4. in + responsible _____irresponsible_____

5. in + legal _____illegal_____

Name _____

Comprehension: Identify Sequence of Events

Write a number in front of each story event to show the sequence
of events in *Where is Carter?*

___5___ **a.** Jessica and Oliver travel to the future.

___2___ **b.** Oliver saw Carter vanish.

___4___ **c.** Jessica takes Oliver to the lab and explains
that they were tinkering with time travel.

___3___ **d.** Oliver looked for Carter at the basketball court.

___1___ **e.** Carter's cell phone rang during breakfast.

**Write two smaller events that took place between the 4th event and
the 5th event.**

6. **a.** _Jessica asks who Carter was talking to when he
vanished._

b. _Oliver remembers that they can look up the
records of phone calls on his family cell phone plan._

Grammar: Adverbs That Compare

• The **comparative form** of an adverb compares two actions.
• The **superlative form** compares more than two actions.

**Underline the adverbs that compare. Write *comparative* or
superlative.**

1. Oliver McBride was younger than his brother. _comparative_

2. Jessica tinkered with gadgets the best out of anyone. _superlative_

3. Oliver studied Rockin' Rock more carefully than Carter. _comparative_

Write a sentence with an adverb that compares.

4. _Answers will vary._

Name _____

Vocabulary: Thesaurus/Dictionary/Synonyms
Read the synonyms below for *fidget* and *glumly*.
Write the synonym that completes each sentence.

> **fidget,** *v.–Syn.* stir, twitch, toss
>
> **glumly,** *adv.–Syn.* mournfully, cheerlessly

1. Suji and her mother _____ twitch _____ nervously as the plane approaches its destination.

2. The girl looked _____ mournfully _____ at the fallen bird nest.

3. The losing team sat _____ cheerlessly _____ on the bench.

4. We _____ toss _____ and turn at night because the mattress is so uncomfortable.

Phonics: Absorbed Prefixes
Say the sentences below and circle the words with a prefix. Write the base word.

1. After the accident, he was (immobile) for awhile. _____ mobile _____

2. Driving without a seatbelt on is (illegal.) _____ legal _____

3. A magnet can (attract) different metals. _____ tract _____

4. Some directions tell you to match the word with the (corresponding) picture. _____ responding _____

Comprehension: Identify Sequence of Events
Read the paragraph. Then, complete the sequence of events.

When I walked toward the exhibit, I felt as if I was traveling back to Ancient Egypt. Inside, I began to pretend that a pyramid fit for a pharaoh was being built. Workers stood around me creating a ramp to transport the pyramid blocks. Huge limestone blocks were carried from quarries to the base of the pyramid. Then, a group of workers polished the blocks. Other workers pushed the blocks up ramps to the correct positions. Finally, an architect used a rope to check the placement. I focused again and realized I was only in the museum.

Building a Pyramid

1. Workers create a ramp to transport blocks.

2. Huge limestone blocks were carried to the pyramid base.

3. A group of workers polished the blocks by hand.

4. Workers help push blocks to the correct position.

5. An architect checked the placement.

Grammar: Adverbs That Compare
Rewrite each sentence. Use the correct form of the adverb in parentheses.

1. Owen hopped into the seat of the time travel machine (faster/fastest) than Rory or Marcos.

   Owen hopped into the seat of the time travel machine faster than Rory or Marcos.

2. "What's our destination?" Rory asked (more glumly/most glumly) than usual.

   "What's our destination?" Rory asked more glumly than usual.

Vocabulary: Word Parts/Latin and Greek Word Parts

- The Latin root **port** means *to carry*. The Latin root **dorm** means *to sleep*.

1. Write a sentence using the words *transport* or *import*. Use a dictionary for support.

   Answers will vary.

2. Find the definition of the word *dormitory* in a dictionary. Then use it in a sentence.

   Answers will vary.

Phonics: Greek Suffixes

Add the correct Greek suffix to create a new word. Use the definition to help. Write the new word on the line.

-logy = study of	**-ician = specialist in**	**-crat = to rule or govern**

Definitions

1. zoo _____zoology_____ study of animals

2. polit _____politician_____ specialist in politics

3. demo _____democracy_____ a government by the people

4. musico _____musicology_____ study of music

Name _____

Comprehension: Identify Problem and Solution

- A **problem** is a question that needs to be solved or answered.
- A **solution** is a way to fix or answer the problem.

Write the solution, or explain why there is not a solution.

Possible answers:

1. **Problem:** People saw lines scratched into the ground, but questioned what pattern these lines created.

   Solution: _Flying above this area allowed people to see_ _that the lines had a special design._

2. **Problem:** Scientists questioned how the difficult task of moving many stones had been accomplished.

   Solution: _After studying, scientists realized that many_ _people must have worked together for many years._

3. **Problem:** Anthropologists question who the creators of the desert drawings are, since they look like drawings made by people in other parts of Peru.

   Explanation: _Anthropologists don't have good records_ _to study._

Grammar: Negatives

- A **negative** word is a word that means "no." It is not correct to have a **double negative**, or more than one "no" word in a sentence.

Write each sentence with the correct word in parentheses.

1. Anthropologists can't find (any/no) evidence.

   Anthropologists can't find any evidence.

2. Nobody (can/can't) say for sure what the lines mean.

   Nobody can say for sure what the lines mean.

Name _____

Vocabulary: Word Parts/Latin and Greek Word Parts

Use the list of Latin and Greek word parts to choose a word in parentheses. Write the correct word to complete each sentence.

Latin and Greek Word Parts

bio = life	**non** = not	**hemi** = half
mem = remember	**phon** = sound	

1. I received a (telephone, memory) call from my uncle. _telephone_

2. He lives in the southern (biosphere, hemisphere), near Santiago, Chile. _hemishere_

3. My uncle has a good (memory, telephone) of his childhood. _memory_

4. So, he decided to undertake the immense task of writing a (euphony, nonfiction) book about the history of our family. _nonfiction_

Phonics: Greek Suffixes

Say each word on the left. Read the chart on the right and underline the Greek suffix in each word.

1. musician

2. logical

3. archaeology

4. biologist

Suffix	Meaning
al	pertaining to
ician	expert in
ist	expert in
logy	study of

Comprehension: Identify Problem and Solution
Answer the questions about the paragraph below.

Two friends, Mike and Lisa, live in different states. They both use e-mail or the telephone to communicate. Last summer, Mike went on a long hike through the countryside of Spain. Mike could not use a cell phone or send e-mails. He bought postcards along the route and sent them to Lisa. When the cards arrived, Lisa knew how Mike was doing.

1. **Problem:** Mike and Lisa live in different states.
   Solutions:

   a. _They write e-mails to each other._

   b. _They make telephone calls._

2. **a.** What was Mike's problem on his hiking trip?

   He was unable to send e-mails or make telephone calls.

   b. How did he solve the problem?

   He wrote postcards.

Grammar: Negatives
Underline the negative word in each sentence.

1. <u>Nobody</u> owns portable typewriters anymore because they are a nuisance to carry.

2. They <u>aren't</u> as good as computers for keeping in touch.

3. A computer will <u>never</u> be as good as a simple postcard.

4. <u>No</u> postcard gives more pleasure than one you get from a friend.

Write a sentence with a negative.

5. _Answers will vary._

Name _____

Vocabulary: Word Parts/Latin Roots
Choose one or more meanings for each word below.

Latin Roots

init = to begin	**manus, man** = hand
rupt = break, burst	**script** = write

1. manuscript
   - **a.** handwritten text *(circled)*
   - **b.** manmade object
   - **c.** ancient writing
   - **d.** manual job

2. initial
   - **a.** continual
   - **b.** starting *(circled)*
   - **c.** first letter *(circled)*
   - **d.** between letters

3. scribe
   - **a.** inscription
   - **b.** writer *(circled)*
   - **c.** keyboard
   - **d.** note taker *(circled)*

4. rupture
   - **a.** fortune
   - **b.** nurture
   - **c.** split *(circled)*
   - **d.** fracture *(circled)*

Phonics: Words from Mythology
Say the words. Write each one next to the sentence about its origin.

capitol	martial	nectar	cereal

1. ___cereal___ Ceres was the Roman goddess of grain and agriculture.

2. ___capitol___ Capitoline was one of the hills of ancient Rome on which a temple to honor the god Jupiter was built.

3. ___martial___ Mars was the Roman god of war.

4. ___nectar___ This drink of the gods made you immortal.

Name _____

Comprehension: Text Structure: Description
- An author uses **description** to explain the qualities or characteristics of something.

Answer the questions about descriptions from *How to Be a Publisher*.

1. Describe the steps the author followed to publish her school newspaper called the *Scribe*.

   a. She collected stories. _____

   b. She printed it on a photocopy machine. _____

   c. She sold each copy for five cents. _____

2. Describe how a team of people helps to write a manuscript and complete a project.

   a. Writers and editors write the manuscript. _____

   b. Designers decide how the pages will look. _____

   c. Salespeople make sure every copy is sold. _____

Grammar: Prepositions and Prepositional Phrases
- A **prepositional phrase** is a group of words that begins with a preposition and ends with a noun or pronoun. The noun or pronoun that follows the preposition is called the **object of the preposition**.

Circle the prepositions. Underline the objects.

1. With a computer, it is easier to become a publisher.

2. Scribes in the Middle Ages wrote manuscripts by hand!

3. Don't forget to tell your friends about your publication.

Write a sentence with a prepositional phrase.

4. Answers will vary. _____

Name _____

Vocabulary: Word Parts/Latin Roots

Read the Latin roots list below to understand the meanings of the words in parentheses. Write the word that completes each sentence.

Latin Roots

scrib/script = to write	**manu** = hand
form = shape	**ject** = throw

1. What is the (formula, rejection) for creating a good book?

   ___formula___

2. Publishers take (formations, manuscripts) and turn them into books

   or articles. ___manuscripts___

3. A (scribe, manual) is a person whose job it is to copy manuscripts.

   ___scribe___

4. There was a huge pile of (formative, rejected) manuscripts that would not

   be used. ___rejected___

Phonics: Words from Mythology

Read the words from mythology below. Use a dictionary or other resource to find words with these origins. Possible answers:

1. Jove (Roman)   ___jovial___

2. Olympus (Greek) ___Olympics___

3. Muse (Greek)   ___museum___

4. Juno (Roman)   ___June___

5. Pan (Greek)   ___panic___

Name _____

Comprehension: Text Structure: Description
Complete the descriptions about the topic below.

During the 15th century, individual blocks of letters were used to print pages of writing. A large table with compartments for each letter block was used. Every block had one raised letter. Letter blocks were selected and arranged on a separate tray. Blank blocks were used for spaces. Then, ink was applied on top of the blocks. Finally, paper was pressed to the arrangement of letters to print one whole page.

1. Describe the printing table and letter blocks.

   a. It was a large table with compartments for each block

   b. The blocks each had a raised letter.

2. Describe the preparation for printing a page of writing.

   a. Blocks were selected and arranged on a tray.

   b. Ink was applied on top of the blocks.

   c. Paper was pressed to the letters.

Grammar: Prepositions and Prepositional Phrases
Underline the prepositional phrase(s) in each sentence.

1. In the past, newspapers provided the main source of news.

   In the past, of news

2. Many people bought newspapers at newsstands.

   at newsstands

3. Today, readers often get news electronically on the Internet.

   on the Internet

Write a sentence with a prepositional phrase.

4. Answers will vary.

Name _____

Vocabulary: Dictionary/Multiple-Meaning Words

- A **multiple-meaning word** is a word with more than one meaning. *Bolt* is a multiple-meaning word.

Write the number of the correct meaning next to each sentence.

bolt	**1:** cylindrical screw with a head at one end and a nut at the other
	2: a flash of lightning
	3: to move or spring suddenly

1. During an electrical storm you see the bolts but don't hear the thunder. ___2___

2. The bolts I got to fasten the trellis to the posts are too short. ___1___

3. If the dog sees a cat, she is going to bolt. ___3___

Phonics: Words from Around the World

Say the words which come from different parts of the world. Then choose the correct word to complete each sentence.

| apricot | chocolate | caribou | plaza | gondola |

1. _____Plaza_____ is a Spanish word than means town square.

2. _____Caribou_____ is a word of Canadian French origin for a type of deer.

3. _____Apricot_____ is a word that comes from Arabic.

4. _____Chocolate_____ is a word that comes from Nahuatl, the language of the Aztec people in Mexico.

5. _____Gondola_____ is an Italian word for the boats on the canals of Venice.

Name _____

Comprehension: Analyze Theme

• The **theme** is the most important idea in a piece of writing.

Answer the questions about *Escape from the Volcano*.

1. How did Seth feel about his older brother, Jed? How do you know this?

   Possible answer: He admired him. He was excited
   to have a day alone with Jed.

2. Predict what will happen to Seth, Jed, and Sarah.

   I predict that
   Possible answer: Seth will guide Jed and Sarah home.

Circle the letter of the answer.

3. What theme fits the events in the story so far?

   a. A Drowsy Day without Chores

   b. Courage During an Emergency

   c. A Hike Down a Mountainside

Grammar: Sentence Combining with Adjectives, Adverbs, and Prepositional Phrases

• Two sentences can be combined by adding an **adjective**, **adverb**, or **prepositional phrase** to one sentence.

Underline the adjective, adverb, or prepositional phrase in the second sentence of each pair. Then combine the sentences.

1. Seth admired Jed. He admired him greatly.

   Seth greatly admired Jed.

2. Sarah picked blackberries. The berries were juicy.

   Sarah picked juicy blackberries.

3. Their eyes itched. They itched from vapors.

   Their eyes itched from vapors.

Vocabulary: Dictionary/Multiple-Meaning Words

Read the sentences below. Write the multiple-meaning word that completes each sentence.

Multiple-Meaning Words

lounge	smoke	fast

1. The volcano began to ____smoke____.

2. People were sitting in the hotel ____lounge____ when Mount St. Helens erupted.

3. The ____fast____ lava poured quickly down the mountain.

4. She decided to ____fast____, or stop eating, in memory of those who lost their lives during the eruption.

Write a sentence using a multiple-meaning word from above.

5. ____Answers will vary.____

Phonics: Words from Around the World

Choose the word to complete each sentence.

1. An (iguana, igloo) is a shelter built with hard snow. ____igloo____

2. He banged the (denim, gong), which summoned the guests to dinner.
____gong____

3. We bought many fun items from the street (bazaar, bronco) in Turkey.
____bazaar____

4. We ate a lot of (pizza, sombrero) and spaghetti at the restaurant.
____pizza____

Name _____

Comprehension: Analyze Theme
Answer the questions related to the theme below.

In 1980, Mount Saint Helens erupted and surprised many people. Homes and forests were destroyed. Afterward, people who lived in the area chose new locations for their homes. Now, scientists closely watch Mount Saint Helens for future eruptions. People are happier knowing they are safer.

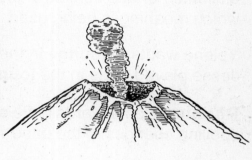

1. What happened when Mount Saint Helens erupted in 1980?

   a. People were surprised.
   _____

   b. Homes and forests were destroyed.
   _____

2. Write a theme that relates to the main idea of the paragraph.

   Being prepared _____ Possible answer: prevents disaster _____

Grammar: Sentence Combining with Adjectives, Adverbs, and Prepositional Phrases
Write the word that completes each sentence. Then combine the sentences.

> early   in ash   big

1. Volcanoes seem to have tempers. Their tempers are _____ big. _____

   Volcanoes seem to have big tempers.
   _____

2. Volcanoes can bury dwellings. They bury them _____ in ash. _____

   Volcanoes can bury dwellings in ash.
   _____

3. Today, scientists can warn people. They warn them _____ early. _____

   Today, scientists can warn people early.
   _____

Name _____

Vocabulary A **multiple-meaning word** is a word that has more than one meaning. You can find the different meanings in a dictionary or use context clues in the text to help you understand which meaning is being used.

Yelena wants to **lounge** in the sun today. (*lounge* means "lie down")
Jesse played darts in the **lounge**. (*lounge* means "a room for recreation")

Phonics Some words have **absorbed prefixes**, or prefixes that cause spelling changes in the base word that they are added to.

Prefix	Base Word	Spelling Change
in- con-	migrated mission	immigrated commission

Comprehension Many fiction and nonfiction texts include **problems** that characters or people solve, or find a **solution** to.

Problem	Larisa had forgotten to do two assignments. Both were due the next day. After school, she had basketball practice.
Solution	Larissa could ask her coach if she could miss basketball practice. Larissa could also leave practice early to begin her homework.

Grammar You can **combine** two short **sentences** with adjectives, adverbs, and prepositional phrases to make a smoother, more interesting sentence.

Short Sentences	Combined Sentences
She is a basketball player. She is a star player.	She is a star basketball player.
The manuscript was finished. Charlie finished the manuscript.	The manuscript was finished by Charlie.

© Macmillan/McGraw-Hill

Name _____

Match the vocabulary words with their meanings.

1. recommend __d__   a. imagined

2. envisioned __a__   b. trying to be a success

3. unsteady __c__   c. changeable

4. ambitious __b__   d. suggest

Circle the word that has a prefix similar to *in-* or *con-* in each group.

5. (immigrated)   retreat   penniless

6. predict   (commissioned)   deliver

Decide whether each word in bold print is an adjective or an adverb.

7. Enrique **formally** introduced Benita to his grandfather.

   a. adjective   (b.) adverb

8. Natalie has **shiny**, **black** hair and **green** eyes.

   (a.) adjective   b. adverb

Fill in the correct end punctuation and quotation marks. Then answer the questions.

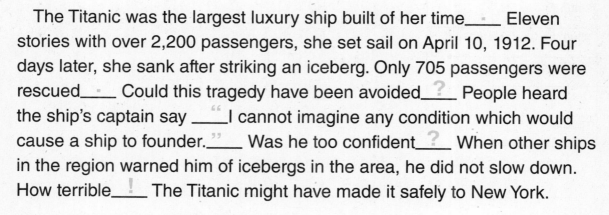

   The Titanic was the largest luxury ship built of her time__.__ Eleven stories with over 2,200 passengers, she set sail on April 10, 1912. Four days later, she sank after striking an iceberg. Only 705 passengers were rescued__.__ Could this tragedy have been avoided__?__ People heard the ship's captain say ____"I cannot imagine any condition which would cause a ship to founder."__ Was he too confident__?__ When other ships in the region warned him of icebergs in the area, he did not slow down. How terrible__!__ The Titanic might have made it safely to New York.

What is the theme of this paragraph?

Take warning seriously.
_____

Phonics: Absorbed Prefixes

Read the story. Circle the words that have the prefixes *in-* and *con-*.
Sometimes, the prefixes may be spelled differently. Read the story
a second time. Then answer the questions.

Jae-Min liked to read science fiction stories about time travel. They made
him (impatient) to learn more about the past and future. He wished he could
travel through time. He would (commute) between centuries and (improve) the
past. He would (conserve) the environment and save it from pollution. He would
advise kings and make war (illegal).

Jae-Min would (investigate) his family, too. His family (immigrated)
to America, so he would return to Asia and (connect) with his
ancestors. Jae-Min would do research about his ancestors to
learn about their lives and work. Jae-Min wondered what he
would find. Would it change his future?

Comprehension: Theme

1. What is the theme of the story?

   Learning about the past might change the future.

2. Draw and complete a Theme Chart for this story.

Setting	
What the Characters Want	
Plot Problem	
Outcome	
Theme	

   Setting—the present;
   Characters Want—to travel to
   the past;
   Problem—learn about ancestors;
   Outcome—wondering about
                     the future;
   Theme—Learning about the past
                might change the future.

Name _____

Vocabulary
Circle the letter of the word to complete each sentence.

1. Michelangelo's painting on the ceiling of the Sistine Chapel was intricate and the details were ____.

   a. examined   **b.** connected

   c. elaborate   **d.** infinite

2. Freya's plane had to stop in St. Louis before it reached its final____ in Atlanta.

   a. aviation   **b.** destination   **c.** revolution   **d.** appreciation

3. The squeaky kitchen door was a ____ until we finally fixed it.

   a. nuisance   **b.** pet   **c.** thrill   **d.** repair

4. Sia felt ____ because she visited the Oval Office of the White House and met the President.

   a. punished   **b.** privileged   **c.** preoccupied   **d.** exhausted

Choose the correct meaning for the multiple-meaning word underlined in each sentence.

5. Peter wanted to <u>lounge</u> on the grass during his day off.

   a. a room for recreation   **b.** to lie down

6. Lydia posted the <u>notice</u> about the important event on the bulletin board.

   a. an announcement   **b.** to pay attention to

Phonics: Absorbed Prefixes
Circle the word that has a prefix like *in-* or *con-* in each group.

7. formally   immigrated   scribes

8. revised   unsteady   commissioned

Grammar: Sentence Combining with Adjectives, Adverbs, and Prepositional Phrases; Negatives

Decide whether the words in italics are adjectives or adverbs. Circle the letter of the answer.

1. Sarah saw *dark* smoke and *black* ashes rising thickly from the top of the mountain.

   a. adjectives   **b.** adverbs

2. Félipa *formally* recommended her friend for the astronaut job.

   a. adjective   **b.** adverb

Circle the prepositional phrase or phrases in each sentence.

3. Did a flying saucer appear above Lao's house and then disappear?

4. They immigrated from across the ocean and could be heard cheering as they landed.

Choose the correct negative form of each sentence. Circle the letter of the answer.

5. The anthropologist could see something in the cave.

   a. The anthropologist could see nothing in the cave.

   b. The anthropologist couldn't see none in the cave.

6. For the philosophers in the Renaissance, there were some obstacles.

   a. For the philosophers in the Renaissance, there weren't no obstacles.

   b. For the philosophers in the Renaissance, there were no obstacles.

7. The scribe could see there was someone home.

   a. The scribe could see there was no one home.

   b. The scribe could see there wasn't nobody home.

Name _____

Editing: Using Commas with Introductory Words and Phrases, End Punctuation, Quotations
Read the letter. Look for errors with punctuation, including quotation marks. Circle the errors and make the corrections on the lines.

1. **Estrella,** _____ Dear Mayor (Estrella)

2. **teenager.** _____ I first moved into Riverton many years ago, when I was a (teenager!) There was an old community center that had ping-pong tables, a kitchen, and chairs and tables where we could play board games. It was

3. **terrific!** _____ (terrific?) Now, our teenagers have nowhere to go in the evening.

4. **use.** _____ I suggest we do fundraising and construct a new building for everyone in the community to (use?) The clubs, youth, and senior citizens of Riverton will have a place to meet and enjoy interesting activities.

5. **"Make... children."** _____ My father used to say (Make) Riverton a place where people will want to raise their (children.) I agree. I hope you will, too.

6. **Sincerely,** _____ (Sincerely)
Rita Rodriguez

Comprehension: Description, Problem and Solution

1. Describe the community center that Rita Rodriguez used when she was a teenager.

   It was an old building, had ping-pong tables, a kitchen, chairs, tables, and board games.

2. Read the story again. What is the problem? What is the solution that Rita Rodriguez suggests?

   Problem—there is no community center for youths.

   Solution—Rita Rodriguez wants to do fundraising and build one.